W9-ADZ-119

DISCARDED

FAMILIAR REPTILES
AND AMPHIBIANS
OF AMERICA

Familiar REPTILES

by WILL BARKER

Drawings by
John Cameron Yrizarry

and AMPHIBIANS

of AMERICA

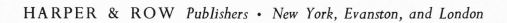

HARPER & ROW *Publishers* • *New York, Evanston, and London*

FAMILIAR REPTILES AND AMPHIBIANS OF AMERICA

FIRST EDITION

LIBRARY OF CONGRESS CATALOG NUMBER: 62-14599

For Ellen and Malcolm Marshall,
ever kind and ever helpful

CONTENTS

FOREWORD

by Alfred Stefferud

Editor, *Yearbook of Agriculture*,
U.S. Department of Agriculture

A great adventure story, which people have retold for nineteen centuries, relates how Aeneas fled from ancient Troy and after many experiences on land and sea founded the colony that became Rome. At one point, overwhelmed by the activity around him, he paused and said simply, "In all this, I had a large part."

An invitation to all of us to pause and take a larger part in the adventure we are living today is given by Will Barker in *Familiar Reptiles and Amphibians of America*, another of his charming, informative, and exciting—yes, highly exciting—books about the creatures that share the earth with us.

Here—to pick a sample from the many that Will Barker's clear, accurate writing and John Yrizarry's lucid drawings put entrancingly before us—we get to know well the alligator. Most of us already have some acquaintance with this reptile that lays eggs; here we learn where it lives, why it needs protection, what it looks like, and how it mates and makes a nest, where it got its name, how it gets its food, and what role it plays in the plant and animal community. So also the lives and homes of lizards, snakes, turtles, tortoises, salamanders, frogs, and toads are explored and made part of our awareness of life.

Some may think this a book for children because it is clear and simple and devoid of the technician's language. But it is also a book for adults, including technicians. It is to the author's credit that he can distill years of experience and research into a tidy, enjoyable book like this. This is not an easy task.

This is fascinating reading—but why (you ask, and so do I) should one read it in a world engrossed with problems of space, technology, threats of war, and bomb shelters. Will Barker answers this question, too, many times over. He gives one answer when he quotes from Aldo Leopold, "Each species, including ourselves, is a link in many chains." He gives another when he cites the American toad, whose individual value in controlling pests is put at twenty dollars annually, and whose survival is threatened when drainage destroys the places where it breeds.

We can easily find other reasons for saying this subject is important and this book worth our time. Knowledge of any kind is power; and the knowledge of ecology, of the interrelations between man and other creatures, and the mysteries of birth and survival, makes us partners and sharers in a world so full of ideas and living things as to be the greatest adventure of all. Thereby are mind and spirit enlarged, horizons broadened, perceptions deepened, and wisdom extended.

And an even better reason may be this: It's fun.

"Each species, including ourselves,
is a link in many chains."

Aldo Leopold, in *A Sand County Almanac*

INTRODUCTION

The reptiles and amphibians of North America are a diversified lot of cold-blooded animals that hop, crawl, slither, slide, and swim. This diversification is to be expected, for the continent north of the Mexican border is a vast land whose terrain differs greatly from one area to another and whose climate is astonishingly varied. These differences and variations give us plant and animal communities of great dissimilarity.

The Arctic Shelf, where polar bears and arctic foxes roam, is a land of such extreme perpetual cold that reptiles and amphibians cannot exist there. But the arid and semiarid lands of the Southwest, a hostile region for many forms of wildlife, are frequented by some reptiles especially adapted to the terrain. One of these is the varicolored Gila monster, the heaviest lizard in the United States.

Vastly different from the homeland of the Gila monster is the continent's humid, subtropical region—an area that includes the South Atlantic and Gulf states. Here the summer climate is sometimes similar to the equatorial rain-forest climate in precipitation, temperature, and humidity. The plant and animal communities of this area have a considerable share of the continent's reptiles and amphibians. One is the Florida worm lizard, an animal so similar in appearance to the earthworm that at first glance it might be mistaken for one. Another animal of the area is the long-snouted American crocodile. It is found in the United States only at the southernmost tip of Florida, but in Mexico it frequents both coasts. It also ranges on south throughout Central America.

The dry Southwest and the humid Southeast are only two of the many regions in which you can find some of North America's reptiles and amphibians. Not all of these animals are so peculiar to an area as the Gila monster nor so restricted in range as the Florida worm lizard. Forms of the garter snake are found throughout the greater part of the United States, in southern Canada, and in northern Mexico. And in the East, the Middle West, and the Southwest, you are sure to run across a species of box turtle as it plods along on an omnivorous search for food, including a seasonal favorite—the wild strawberry.

The Gila monster, the worm lizard, the American crocodile, the garter snake, and the box turtle with all the other reptiles belong to a class of animals known as the Reptilia. The frogs, the toads, and the salamanders, together with the little-known caecilians, are in another class named the Amphibia. Here is the position of these classes in the vertebrate series:

1. Fishes   (Pisces)
2. AMPHIBIANS   (AMPHIBIA)
3. REPTILES   (REPTILIA)
4. Birds   (Aves)
5. Mammals   (Mammalia)

Each of these classes has its own distinguishing features, which set off its members from those of the other vertebrate classes. In turn, each class is subdivided into smaller groups in a method of systematic classification—or taxonomy—of all plants and animals. Of these groups, the ones most frequently mentioned in this book are:

Class
    Order
        Suborder
            Family
                Genus
                    Species
                        Subspecies

Taxonomy, the science of animal and plant classification, is a necessary device which makes scientific biology possible. The working unit of the taxonomist is the species. A species may be defined as a group of animals or plants that are alike in possessing one or more characteristics distinguishing them from all other organisms.

Each species is identified by two scientific names. The first is the name of the genus to which it belongs. The initial letter of this name is always capitalized. The second name is that of the species. The initial letter of this name is never capitalized. The two names taken together are the scientific name of a species. Thus the name of the American toad is *Bufo americanus*; that is, it belongs to the genus of *Bufo* and to the species *americanus*.

The use of two names for a species is known as the binomial system of nomenclature. It dates from the time of Carolus Linnaeus, the great Swedish botanist who introduced it as a way of classifying animals and plants during the eighteenth century. In some instances a trinomial is used to designate certain kinds of animals. The use of three names is because there is some differentiating feature (a modification) within a species. This modification gives us a subspecies or a geographic variety, form, or race. Thus, the Hudson Bay toad, a far northern form, is designated by the trinomial *Bufo americanus copei*.

A subspecies is the smallest unit in systematic classification. Next comes the species. Taken together they form a genus. All of this next highest group, the genera, combine to make a family. The families taken together make a still larger group known as an order. The orders form a class. And the classes make a phylum. In an ascending scale each succeeding category is larger and more inclusive than the preceding one. Sometimes intermediate steps are introduced, such as the superclass or subphylum.

Starting with the working unit of the taxonomist, the species, the classification of the American toad would read:

Species	: Bufo americanus
Genus	: Bufo
Family	: Bufonidae
Order	: Anura
Class	: Amphibia
Superclass	: Tetrapoda
Subphylum	: Vertebrata
Phylum	: Chordata

The scientific and popular names used throughout this book are those listed in *Common Names of North American Amphibians and Reptiles*, published by the American Society of Ichthyologists and Herpetologists. There have been some changes in the scientific names since the publication of this list. Wherever possible the most recent scientific name is used.

Of the two classes of vertebrates discussed in this book, the amphibians were the first to appear on land. The fossils of these first land vertebrates are common in the swamp deposits that characterize the Carboniferous period—a time when much of the earth's coal was being formed. In this amphibian world of long ago there were giant horsetails—prevalent today in a different form, especially in our northern states—ferns and fernlike trees, and primitive confers known as Cordaites, tall trees distinguished by long, swordlike leaves.

A form of dragonfly, *Meganeura*, darted through the air on wings with a spread of 29 inches; land snails made their slimy ways thither and yon; and cockroaches, differing little from those today, were everywhere. In fact, these insects were so abundant that more than eight hundred species have been described for this period. And it was during this period that the first amphibians appeared.

The ancestors of today's amphibians were on earth about 280 million years ago. They were a group of animals known as the *Labyrinthodonts*. These first amphibians were distinguished by short, stumpy legs, and fishlike tails. But as a result of changes brought about by evolution, descent with change, the amphibians as we now know them came into being.

The word *amphibian* comes from the Greek: *amphi*, meaning "double," and *bios*, meaning "life." And a double life is exactly what a great many of these odd, cold-blooded animals live.

Most of today's amphibians characteristically undergo a metamorphosis—a series of changes in form and structure—from an aquatic to a partially terrestrial form. Once a year these amphibians take a vacation from the land to return to the water. During this stage they breed and the females discharge jellylike eggs in a suitable environment. The water to which this group returns is largely fresh, though some frogs tolerate salt water and one early group of amphibians was entirely marine. The reason most amphibians are unable to adapt to a salt-water existence is explained by Knut Schmidt-Nielsen in his book *Animal Physiology* (1960):

Apparently the skin of the amphibians is so permeable that they cannot evolve a means of eliminating sufficient salt; they have no organ that takes on the role of the fish gill, and their kidney is unable to produce a concentrated urine.

The frogs, toads, salamanders, and their allies are in a way living relicts, providing us with a glimpse into the past. But they are still very active members of the plant and animal communities in which we find them today. And as the English poet John Clare noted in "The Startled Frog," they are an enjoyable part of life:

> I love at early morn, from new-mown swath
>   To see the startled frog his route pursue;
> To mark, while leaping o'er the dripping path,
>   His bright sides scatter dew . . .

The reptiles, descendants of the amphibians, appeared on this planet during the Upper Carboniferous period—possibly some fifty million years after the amphibians first evolved. The first reptiles, known as cotylosaurs, included the species *Seymouria*, which is sometimes described as the last amphibian and sometimes as the first reptile. But however it is classified, *Seymouria* is considered an almost perfect link between the amphibians and the more advanced reptiles.

The predecessors of our snakes, lizards, chameleons, turtles, alligators, and crocodiles were in many instances huge, ungainly creatures. Among them were various dinosaurs, including the carnivorous Theropoda (a name meaning "beast-feet"); flying reptiles such as pterodactyls, whose fossil remains have been found in the chalk formations of Kansas; and the "fish-lizards" or ichthyosaurs.

The dinosaurs, whose name is Greek for "terrible lizard," came in all shapes and sizes. Some were only 2½ feet long; others measured nearly 90 feet. Fossil remains of these early reptiles have been found in rock formations of every continent.

The federal government has set aside an area in the western United States, partly in Utah and partly in Colorado, known as Dinosaur National Monument. In the southwestern part of the Monument is a section called Dinosaur Quarry. Here you can see fossil remains of early reptiles. These fossils are in deposits formed in the Jurassic period—some 140 million years ago. Near the Monument's Visitor Center are many whiptail lizards—so named for their habit of lashing their long, slender tails from side to side as they run.

The reptiles of today are only a remnant of a formerly large animal group. The snakes and other cold-blooded allies are also reminders of the past. And like all living creatures, these scaled, shelled, and leathery-skinned animals live in communities best suited to their needs.

Such communities are not nearly so numerous as they used to be, for man's encroachment has steadily decreased wildlife habitats of all kinds. In particular, continual drainage—euphemistically called land reclamation—is doing away with the types of environment for those reptiles and amphibians, as well as for other animals that require wet lands or water in order to survive.

Survival of species such as the American toad is important—not only because no species should be permitted to become extinct but also because the animal has a well-defined role in its community—and a role that has positive value to man. During its active season this squat brown creature hops about in search of flies, grasshoppers, grubs, slugs, and many other pests, which it consumes by the thousands. The toad devours so many garden and crop pests each season that the annual value of a single toad to the gardener or agriculturist has been set at twenty dollars.

Snakes, too, suffer from destruction of habitat, as well as at the hands of the ignorant who kill them because they consider all snakes a menace. But in their way snakes are as valuable as toads. These reptiles destroy quantities of rats, mice, and other animals categorized as vermin, though some of the good they do is offset by the fact that they also prey on the insect-eating toad.

This book deals with some of our most common and widely distributed reptiles and amphibians, and with others which, though they are well known by name, are rare or restricted in range. The life history of each, its role in the plant and animal community—insofar as that is known—and a description of its appearance will be found in this book.

Today there is so much information available on any subject

that no individual can "know it all." Any number of people and numerous other sources have been consulted in the course of writing this book. I wish to express my thanks to everyone who has helped. If any of the information so generously furnished me is mistakenly presented, the fault is mine.

I wish to express my particular gratitude for the help of several specialists. Ever since I first called upon her in 1952, while I was editing a publication on venomous snakes for the U. S. Fish and Wildlife Service, Dr. Doris M. Cochran, Curator of Reptiles and Amphibians at the United States National Museum in Washington, D. C., has always been ready and willing with her help. The same is true of the other staff members of the Museum, who want to have the facts on any subject presented with the greatest possible exactness. I am indebted to Charles M. Bogert of the American Museum of Natural History for his painstaking reading of this book in manuscript. And Carl Kauffeld of the Staten Island Zoological Park is due a word of thanks in connection with those parts of the manuscript that he read and commented upon.

Special thanks are also due the illustrator of this book. John Yrizarry has a particular fondness for the animals he has drawn for *Familiar Reptiles and Amphibians of America*. The four fine color plates and the many excellent black-and-white drawings not only complement the text but form an integral part of the book.

During the preparation of this book I received help and information from various organizations and institutions, to whom I wish to acknowledge my indebtedness:

National Geographic Society, Washington, D. C.; National Zoological Park and the United States National Museum, Smithsonian Institution; United States Fish and Wildlife Service and Rock Creek Park Nature Center (National Capital Parks), United States Department of the Interior; United States Weather Bureau and Bureau of Vital Statistics, United States Department of Commerce; Educational Materials Laboratory, Office of Education, and Public Health Service, United States Department of Health, Education and Welfare; Missouri State Conservation Commission; Staff, Mt. Pleasant Library, Washington, D.C.

W. B.

Washington, D.C.
January 1964

PART I

Reptiles: LET THE WATERS

BRING FORTH THE CREEPING

CREATURE HAVING LIFE . . .

Genesis 1:20

The reign of the reptiles ended when the last of the dinosaurs died and the mammals became the dominant class of animals. Though the number of reptiles today is small in comparison to the number in prehistoric times, there are still nearly five thousand kinds. These are divided into four orders, one of which consists of a single species. The creature with an order to itself is the tuatara, formerly common in New Zealand but now found only on some nearby coastal islets.

The tuatara, dark olive-green with yellow spines along its back, received its common name from the Maoris. It is a combination of *tua*, "on the farther side" (the back), and *tara*, "spine." Herpetologists are responsible for the scientific name, *Sphenodon punctatum*, a free translation of which is "beakhead." An iguanalike reptile, *S. punctatum* is often referred to as a "living fossil" because it was on earth before the time of the dinosaurs and has outlived them.

Though the tuatara has managed to survive all these years, the *New Standard Encyclopedia* says the order to which it belongs, the Rhynchocephalia, "may be considered extinct." But just possibly the tuatara may not die out, for the New Zealand government has enacted legislation to protect it.

The classification of living reptiles (Reptilia) includes the following orders and suborders, and the members of each:

1. Testudinata	Turtles, tortoises, terrapins
2. Rhynchocephalia	New Zealand lizard (tuatara)
3. Squamata	
Sauria	Lizards
Serpentes	Snakes
4. Crocodilia	Crocodiles, alligators, and allies

The reptiles, first in the series of the higher vertebrates, are animals that never breathe with gills, and that are cold-blooded. For the most part they are oviparous, producing eggs that hatch outside the body. Some, however, are ovoviviparous—that is, the young hatch from eggs inside the body, and are born alive. And still others are viviparous—that is, the young develop within the body and are born alive. The young are born resembling the adults, do not have to undergo a gill-breathing stage during which a metamorphosis takes place, and have to fend for themselves as soon as they hatch or leave the female's body.

The reptiles are distinguished by a protective body covering of scales, horny plates, or horn-covered bony shells. The skin is dry, but the eyes are moist, kept so by special glands. Some reptiles have legs ending in claw-toed feet or flippers; others have only vestigial limbs that are useless; and still others have no limbs at all.

The name of the class to which all these widely differing animals belong derives from the Latin word for "creeping." But this does not accurately describe the means by which North America's seven hundred or so reptiles get about. The various members of this class have their own individual ways of covering the home ranges they inhabit within the plant and animal communities to which they belong.

SNAKES

"Snakes are probably more feared and misunderstood than any other form of our native wildlife . . ."

C. W. Schwartz
Missouri Conservation Commission

Throughout the world there are about three thousand species of snakes. They belong to a suborder in the animal kingdom known as the Serpentes, and are distinguished by a limbless, elongate body covered with scales. These are really horny folds of skin, usually overlapping one another like the shingles on a roof but occasionally lying flat and edge to edge like the tiles of a swimming pool.

The scales on the head, which are often enlarged, form a protective covering of horny plates or shields. The eyes, in which the pupils vary in shape—they may be round, elliptical, or keyholed, to name three of several types—lack movable eyelids. But they are covered by hard, transparent eyecaps. These prevent injury where the ground cover is dense or when a snake is burrowing or swimming. They also account for the fixed, somewhat glittering expression that some people find frightening.

The number of scales on the back and sides of a snake varies greatly from species to species. There may be more than one hundred lengthwise rows, as in the pythons and some boas, or there may be as few as ten in South American snakes of the genus *Ophis*. Sometimes there are sharp differences in size and shape between the scales on the back and those on the sides, and they may be more or less ridged or keeled, depending upon the kind of snake. And sometimes the scales of the back are keeled and those on the sides are smooth.

4

Director Carl Kauffeld of the Staten Island Zoological Park explains the locomotion of snakes in this way: In all terrestrial snakes there is a series of large, transverse scales—overlapping toward the rear—known as "ventrals" or abdominal scutes. Each one of these is associated with a pair of ribs. Inserted on the ribs are retractor and extensor muscles that move these scales backward and forward, thus giving the snake the caterpillar traction which it uses in straight-line progression, by gripping the irregularities of the surface over which it crawls. Almost all land species use this mode of crawling when moving leisurely, but if they are startled into acceleration, most resort to undulation (squirming). A second method which they employ consists of drawing the body into a series of curves and then suddenly straightening out. This is done in quick succession, and has earned the very appropriate name "concertina-locomotion."

The caterpillar mode of progression is virtually useless on a smooth surface, but undulation and concertina-locomotion make it possible for snakes to crawl on any surface, however smooth. Snakes, therefore, are not helpless on glass or any other highly polished, smooth surface, as some people suppose.

Still another method of locomotion, employed by certain desert snakes, is known as "sidewinding." This is an adaptation to loose and shifting sand, and is accomplished by the snake's lifting a portion of the body and literally throwing it ahead of itself; hence the direction taken is inevitably to one side or to the other. Though sidewinding is especially useful in sand, it is equally effective over very smooth surfaces.

The number of times a snake sheds or sloughs off its skin during its yearly active period varies with the species. For some snakes the initial skin-shedding occurs within a few hours after birth or hatching. For others the first skin-shedding may not occur until the snake is six to fourteen days old. Rapid growth is likely to cause more frequent skin-sheddings. Older snakes may shed as often as every two months or as infrequently as twice a year. A wound causes the acceleration of ecdysis, as the process is also called.

Ten days to three weeks before the snake is ready to shed, its eyes become clouded (opaque) and the animal is partially blind. Before the actual shedding takes place the eyes clear and the snake once more has unimpaired vision. Now the snake is ready to shed. It does so by working the skin loose at the point of the chin and the point of the snout, and then slipping it off inside out. This maneuver is accomplished by muscular expansions and contractions and the accompanying wriggling of the skin. Sometimes at the start of the skin-shedding a snake rubs against the ground.

Further distinguishing characteristics of the snake are a lack of limbs, except in a few species that have a rudimentary hind pair; the lack of external ears; and the presence of a single, fully developed lung—except in the Boidae, which have two such lungs. The tongue is forked and is an organ for both tasting and smelling. As a snake slithers over its home grounds, its tongue darts out and in through a notch in the upper jaw.

The tip of the tongue is moist and delicate, and while thrust out usually flicks up and down in a vertical plane. It picks up dust particles and carries them to two small cavities in the roof of the mouth known as Jacobson's organs. These are lined with sensory cells, which transmit sensations to the brain. It is in this way that a snake learns of its surroundings. This is the only function of the tongue, for contrary to an old wives' tale the organ is not an instrument to inflict a sting—nor is it an aid to hearing, as was also formerly believed. And the sense of smell is keen, even without the use of the tongue.

Except for those surrounding the eyes and the brain-case, all the bones of the snake skull are capable of a surprising amount of motion. The jaw bones, upper and lower, are in two sections, a right and a left, and these are capable of independent movement, which is controlled by the action of associated bones at the back of the skull. Since a snake has no teeth for biting off food or for chewing—but only for seizing and holding—it has to swallow all prey whole. And this feat is made possible by the ingenious arrangement of the bones.

The alternate action of the jaw bones—a matter of disengaging the recurved teeth of one side and holding with the other, permits the snake to hook a food morsel into its mouth. In other words, the snake literally "walks over" its food. Because the loosely articulated bones at the back of the skull make possible the lateral as well as vertical dilation of the throat, the snake is able to swallow prey many times its own diameter. Large prey may take from one to several hours to be swallowed, and for some time thereafter the snake is sluggish.

A snake has to kill its prey in the wild, though captives seem to prefer pre-killed food. Snakes employ various methods of securing their food. Nearly all snakes seize small animals and swallow them while they are still struggling; some overpower their prey by pinning them to the ground; others kill by constriction, squeezing the victim until the heart action stops; and still others kill by injecting poison. To drink, a snake submerges its mouth and gulps enough water to slake its thrist.

The reproduction of snakes varies, but is usually either oviparous or ovoviviparous. An oviparous snake produces eggs that hatch after expulsion from the body of the female, whereas an ovoviviparous snake brings forth fully developed young that hatched from eggs retained in the female's body. Most nonpoisonous snakes reproduce by the latter method. Whether the young are hatched or born alive, the number in a brood varies with the species. A few snakes brood their eggs, but none gives its young any parental care; it simply abandons them to circumstance.

Snakes are found in various environments. The majority are terrestrial, but some are burrowers or tree-dwellers, and others are aquatic or marine. The distribution of these clean, cold-bodied animals throughout the world is limited because the temperature of their bodies is entirely subject to the temperature of their surroundings. There are no snakes in areas where the subsoil is permanently frozen. Of the 114 species listed for the United States and Canada, not one is recorded any farther north than the southern limit of Hudson Bay. Mexico, with 336 species, has many more snakes than the United States.

The snakes have left little in the way of a fossil record because the body skeleton is so simplified and the bones are so delicate and loosely connected. Though paleontological details are lacking, there is a great deal of information regarding the long association of snakes with man and his activities. The record is a composite of fact and fancy, with some of the latter still accepted as truth by many people. One such bit of fancy common here and in England, and probably other countries too, is that a snake never dies until the sun goes down, however much it may have been cut to pieces.

In *Strange Superstitions and Magical Practices*, William J. Fielding writes, "The serpent has symbolized both evil and good, being associated in some religious legends with temptation and sin; in others with wisdom and immortality; in all cases with subtlety and magical effectiveness."

The snake appears in connection with the beliefs of early Egyptians. One of their protective divinities was Buto, the snake-goddess and ancient protectress of Lower Egypt. She was frequently represented in the form of a cobra—a snake still present in Egypt and bearing the scientific name *Naja haje*. This is one of several species used in snake-charming—an ancient and popular practice that can still be seen throughout the East. The venom of the cobra is similar to that of the coral snakes in the southern United States.

Before the time of the Greeks, the Babylonians had a symbol in the form of a winged staff around which serpents were entwined. This symbol was related to other serpent symbols, including one of healing. Later on the Greek god Hermes, considered the benefactor of mankind, was depicted holding such a staff—known as the caduceus. It eventually replaced the one-snake symbol of Asclepius, Greek god of the healing art. And since 1902 the caduceus has been the insignia of all personnel of the medical branch of the United States Army.

In that part of the New World now known as Mexico, the Aztecs worshiped a serpent-god named Quetzalcoatl; he was "the master of life." In a Mexican religious calendar of the sixteenth century he is depicted in the act of swallowing a man. North of the Rio Grande, in what is now northeastern Arizona, the Hopi Indians today, as their ancestors did before them, perform a ritual known as the snake dance. During this ceremony, a petition for rain, the participants handle live rattlesnakes—one group of poisonous snakes found in North America.

POISONOUS SNAKES

RATTLESNAKES
Crotalus and *Sistrurus*

". . . but the good God has marked the beast by putting a *cloche* (bell) on its tail."

ERNEST THOMPSON SETON's *Arctic Prairies*

The *cloche*, or bell, referred to by Ernest Thompson Seton is the "trademark" of the rattlesnake—a snake represented in North America by twenty-nine species and more than sixty subspecies, according to Charles M. Bogert of the American Museum of Natural History. In one form or another this venom-injecting snake is widely though not uniformly distributed. Its range begins in southernmost Canada and extends southward throughout the greater part of the United States and on into Mexico. Some areas, such as Arizona, have several species; others, such as the Pacific Northwest, have no more than one; and still others have none—one such area being the Bitterroot Valley along the Montana-Idaho border.[1]

The rattlesnake belongs to a family of heavy-bodied snakes known as the Viperidae, and is in a subfamily named the Crotalinae. All such snakes have vertically elliptical pupils similar to those in the eyes of cats, and all have a deep pit on each side of the head. These pits, located between the eye and the nostril, are sensory organs. They aid the snake in locating warm-blooded prey. If the pits are covered, the snake does not strike accurately, sometimes even missing its prey completely.

United States Fish and Wildlife Service herpetologist William H. Stickel[2] says, "If a snake does not have pits and vertical pupils, you can be sure it is not a rattler, copperhead, or cottonmouth."

---

[1] For the distribution of our poisonous snakes, see *Field Book of Snakes of the United States and Canada*, by K. P. Schmidt and D. D. Davis (G. P. Putnam's Sons, New York, 1941).

[2] *Venomous Snakes of the United States and Treatment of Their Bites*, Wildlife Leaflet 339, U. S. Fish and Wildlife Service, U. S. Department of the Interior, June 1941.

The last two snakes—the copperhead or upland moccasin and the cottonmouth or water moccasin—belong to another genus of pit vipers. The only other truly venomous snakes in North America are the coral snakes. They are small-headed, with slender bodies, and their eyes have round pupils. And they lack the pits that distinguish the moccasins and rattlesnakes.

The easiest way to recognize most rattlesnakes is by the vibration of its rattle—the *cloche*, bell, buzzer, or whirrer that gives warning of the animal's presence. The rattling of a small species can be heard only a short distance, but that of a large one carries several feet. Not all rattlers, however, "sound off" before striking, though they do so as a general rule. And juveniles and those without rattles are soundless.

A newly hatched rattler has a little "prebutton" on the tip of its somewhat blunted tail. This button is lost when the young snake sheds its skin for the first time, within a week or ten days after birth, and a real button is exposed. From then on, each time a rattler sloughs off its old outer skin, a new segment is added, pushing the button farther back from the tip of the tail. In time the snake has a string of jointed and loosely interlocking segments.

A partially grown young rattler is likely to have a tapered string, whereas an adult usually has a string in which the rattles are of uniform size. Though strings of rattles help to differentiate a young snake from an old one, they are not an aid in telling how old individuals are. Hardly any rattlesnake has a complete string, for rattles are frequently worn away or broken off.

As soon as it is born a rattlesnake of any species is able to strike and inflict a painful wound. The venom is predominantly composed of hemotoxins (blood poisons) that destroy tissue, make the blood clot too much or too little, and lower the body's resistance to infection. In addition the venom contains some neurotoxins. The amounts of these nerve-destroying toxins vary with the species of rattlesnake, and usually those that strike people or cattle are not likely to have a large amount of the highly neurotoxic venom.

The venom is injected by means of fangs—teeth that have become enlarged, hollow, and curved so that they are effective in the same way as hypodermic needles. A fang is attached to a movable bone on each side of the upper jaw. Each fang folds flat against the roof of the mouth and is sheathed in a fleshy casing that covers all but the tip. Alongside each functional fang are others in varying stages of development. A new set of these reserve fangs replaces the old one every few weeks.

The venom pumped through the hollow fangs is contained in glands at the sides of the head and just behind the inner ear. Each gland has a duct, or canal, that runs to the base of each fang, where it joins an opening leading into the fang canals.

Striking is accomplished by a sudden, lightning-quick straightening of the forward part of the body, held in an S-shape by a snake on the defensive. Though a strike is usually equal to about one-third of the snake's length, it may be as much as one-half this length or slightly more. In order to effect a strike equal to its entire length, the snake must have its tail braced against some solid object, such as the base of a stump or a rock. A downhill strike is also likely to be as long as the snake itself. A rattler does not have to brace in order to strike; it can do so from any position and even while in the water, where it occasionally swims with the tail erect.

When a rattler strikes, the fangs spring forward as the jaws open at the time of contact with the victim. The muscles of the glands force the venom into the canals connected with the fang openings, and it then flows into the punctures in the skin of the victim. In addition to the fang punctures, the skin may also show the imprint of the two rows of small teeth in the roof of the mouth and those in the lower jaw. If both fangs and all the teeth are in play, the wound of a rattler or other pit viper looks something like this:

fang punctures are slightly larger than those made by the teeth.

In 1959 the Bureau of Vital Statistics, U. S. Department of Health, Education and Welfare, reported thirteen deaths from snakebite in the United States. Of this number, nine died from rattlesnake bites. Among the nine, some undoubtedly succumbed to the bite of the diamondback rattler, represented by three species:

the eastern, *Crotalus adamanteus*, the western, **C.** *atrox*, and the red, **C.** *ruber* found in California.

The range of the eastern diamondback starts in the vicinity of Pamlico River and Sound, in east-central North Carolina, and extends south to include all of Florida and west into Louisiana. This species seems to have a preference for palmetto flatwoods, though it also frequents most low, brushy regions on its range—a coastal strip about one hundred miles wide.

The western diamondback, essentially a reptile of arid and semiarid regions, ranges from central Missouri and eastern Texas west into southeastern California. The range is then south through Sonora in western Mexico and as far south as San Luis Potosí in the eastern part of this country. This reddish or yellow-gray rattler, dotted with brown diamond-shaped spots, has the regional name "coon tail" because its tail is ringed in black and white.

The eastern diamondback, largest of the rattlesnakes, is an olive or grayish-green reptile distinguished by diamond-shaped markings on the back. They are edged in yellow, a color in a somewhat duller hue that occurs on the belly. Its usual length is 5 to 6 feet, though there is a recorded measurement for one of 7 feet 3 inches, exclusive of the rattle, and another, reported by herpetologist Raymond L. Ditmars, was 8 feet 3 inches. Usually the western diamondback is smaller and lighter than the eastern. It is a matter or record, however, that one western diamondback did measure 7 feet 5 inches, though the average length is less than 5 feet.

How long the eastern and other species live in the wild is unknown, though there are good estimates based on the field studies made in California by Henry S. Fitch. It is a matter of record that the life span of a captive Pacific rattlesnake was twenty years— perhaps the result of living under optimum conditions.

The chances of survival for a young eastern diamondback are not great. Out of a live-born litter of twelve, few survive the first winter. Hawks of all kinds, the various skunks, and the snake-eating snakes prey on the young. Hogs stamp many young rattlers to death, and it is thought that doe deer sometimes kill rattlers in the same way in order to protect fawns. And some young snakes starve, while others freeze, and still others die from exposure to the heat.

The body temperature of the diamondback, like that of all other

**TIMBER
RATTLESNAKE**
Crotalus horridus; yellow phase

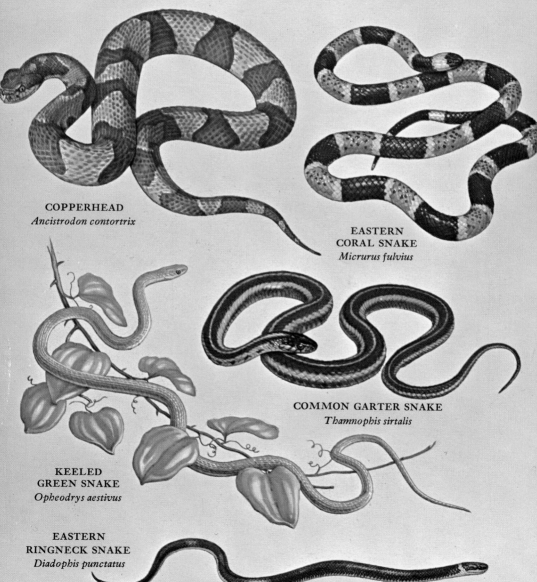

COPPERHEAD
Ancistrodon contortrix

**EASTERN
CORAL SNAKE**
Micrurus fulvius

COMMON GARTER SNAKE
Thamnophis sirtalis

**KEELED
GREEN SNAKE**
Opheodrys aestivus

**EASTERN
RINGNECK SNAKE**
Diadophis punctatus

cold-blooded animals, is affected by prevailing temperatures. This is the reason a diamondback shifts from one spot to another, for even short exposure to intense heat is fatal. A desert species (*C. cerastes*) died within seven minutes after being placed on warm sand in the sun when the temperature of the air registered 96° F.

To escape death from winter's extreme cold, the eastern diamondback and its relatives hibernate. In areas where the snowfall is heavy, most snakes are able to winter in safety if they are two or three feet beneath the earth's surface. The interval of hibernation depends upon the severity and length of the winter. The snakes in the North sometimes remain inactive as long as nine months. Those in the South may hibernate only a few weeks. The eastern diamondback, like any other snake, passes this quiescent interlude in what may be described as "a greatly reduced rate of living."

Like all snakes, upon emerging from hibernation the eastern diamondback is unusually active, so spring is the time of year to be especially on the alert when you are in snake country. Upon emerging from hibernation, the eastern diamondback searches for prey. The mainstay of its diet is the eastern cottontail rabbit. After locating one, it strikes so rapidly that an observer sees nothing but the result. The rabbit bounds forward, rolls on its side, kicks convulsively as the venom takes effect, then dies.

Another species of rattlesnake is found throughout the eastern half of the United States. This is *C. horridus*, the banded, timber, or canebrake rattler. In some form, or color phase, it ranges from central Vermont south into Georgia, and west into Iowa, Kansas, and eastern Texas. It is numerous in the mountains of Massachusetts, southern New York, and eastern Pennsylvania. Anyone hiking the Appalachian Trail should be on the lookout for its warning buzz.

The most usual color phase of this rattlesnake is a sulphur yellow, banded with streaks of dark brown or black. The bands may be wavy and sharply pointed at the rear, or broken into a series of splotches. It was a rattler of this type which prompted the *New York Times* to headline a 1961 item:

RITUAL WITH SNAKE FATAL TO MOTHER

The Associated Press story, datelined Iager, West Virginia, September 29, was the story of Columbia Gay Chafins Hagerman's first and only attempt at snake-handling. During services at the Church in Jesus, Jolo, West Virginia, Mrs. Hagerman became ill three minutes after being bitten by what the lay preacher described as a "yellow timber rattler." She died six days later, the victim of a test of faith based on the Gospel According to St. Mark (16:17–18): ". . . In my name . . . they shall take up serpents." Though the handling of snakes in connection with religious services has been outlawed in many states, such is not the case in West Virginia. Therefore no charges could be filed.

The average length of the "yellow timber rattler" is 3 feet 8 inches. There are records of specimens measuring 5 feet 1 inch, and 6 feet 2 inches. One of the measured specimens had a rattle with ten uniform segments.

The banded rattlesnake is a snake of rocky areas—ledges that are fissured and outcroppings that are shelved. Before Indian summer sets in, the rattlers of an area gather at some rocky outpost. They spend hours in the sun, which at this season is not so hot as to be dangerous. But as the days become shorter and the nights grow chillier, the snakes retreat deep into rocky fissures to over-winter in safety. When the season for hibernating is over they emerge, but remain in the vicinity of the wintering quarters for days-on-end. This stay-at-home spring interlude is the mating season. Once the next generation is assured, the individuals disperse to rock-stewn home ranges adjacent to the hibernating spot. On an individual home range, the banded rattlesnake hunts for the young of ground-nesting birds and for mice, rats, rabbits, and squirrels.

The female brings forth live young, as is the way with all the rattlesnakes. The number in a brood varies from seven to twelve. A female of the black phase may have a brood in which there are both black and yellow color phases. A yellow female may also have a litter that contains both color phases. As a rule the black phase seems to be a characteristic of the males.

Another snake with a wide distribution is the prairie rattlesnake, a subspecies. The range of this rattler extends from the Great Plains at about the 96th meridian to the Rocky Mountains, and from southernmost Canada south into Texas. This rattler is smaller and

Prairie Rattlesnake,
Crotalus viridis viridis

less heavy-bodied than either the timber or the diamondback species. The average length for one of these greenish snakes is about 3 feet 2 ½ inches. It is distinguished by a dark line that starts from beneath the center of the eye and extends to the corners of the mouth. The line has a border of white on each edge, and the border to the front is about the width of a row of scales.

Among rattlers this species is a great wanderer. It is also one that is ever ready to strike. Raymond L. Ditmars wrote, "Few rattlesnakes throw as much energy into the fighting coil as this species. When surprised it flings its body into circular formation, raises the neck some distance from the loose coils in the form of a sharply oblique bow, and jabs at the enemy."

The other group of rattlesnakes in North America are the dwarf or pigmy species of the genus *Sistrurus*. They are distinguished by having the top of the head covered with a symmetrical arrangement of large shields. These rattlesnakes fall into two groups: one has a small, slender tail ending in a miniscule rattle; the other has a short, stout tail tipped by a good-sized rattle.

The pigmy rattlesnake (*S. miliarius*) is found from the vicinity of Charleston, South Carolina, south throughout parts of Georgia and Alabama. It is replaced in Florida by the subspecies *S. m. barbouri*, and in Oklahoma and Texas by another subspecies, *S. m. streckeri*.

These tiny rattlers are ever on the defensive, signaling their presence by vibrating the tail at a furious rate. If you disregard this warning and move closer, the little reptile makes short, tentative strikes. Though the amount of venom a pigmy rattler is able to inject is not so great as that of the larger species, it is still potent and therefore dangerous.

The largest rattlesnake in the genus *Sistrurus* is the massasauga, known, too, as the ground rattlesnake. The most common color phase of this species is grayish brown, splotched with darker brown patches faintly outlined in white. There is a well-developed rattle at the end of the stout tail, whose upper surface has alternating bands of grayish brown and dark brown.

The massasauga (*S. catenatus*) frequents a variety of habitats, including swamps and bogs from western New York to southeastern Arizona and from southernmost Canada to Kansas. It is also found on islands off the coast of Texas. Thoughout this territory it is not so numerous as it used to be, for it does not do well where there is intense cultivation of the land. It is also probably the victim of the drainage of wetland areas—source of frogs for which it seems to have a perference. In fact, as long ago as 1913 Edward T. Whiffen wrote in the *New York Zoological Society Bulletin*:

The Massasauga, a species of dwarf rattlesnake, is still to be found in New York State, in and around Cicero Swamp . . . Older residents assured me that the snake is much less common than formerly . . . Its disappearance is due probably to ceaseless slaughter and the draining of the swamp.

According to Mr. Whiffen, the massasaugas of this area usually had six to eight rattles, though the region did produce specimens with ten rattles and one with sixteen. This species is ordinarily much more modest when it comes to rattles. A female measuring 2 feet 2 inches had only five rings to her rattle. She was small, for a more average size is about a yard from tip of snout to tip of tail. But no matter what the size, the venom of this rattlesnake is highly toxic—a state of affairs that places it on the dangerous list.

The massasauga, a live-bearing species, gets its name from that of an Indian tribe known as the Missisauga—an Objibway word whose literal meaning is, "It has a big mouth."

Forty-eight years after Mr. Whiffen wrote his observations on the massasauga in 1913, Russell Allen, a University of Oklahoma Medical Center research fellow, was trying to learn why rattlers get rattled. His observations, as reported March 3, 1961 in the Washington *Star*, "indicated people make the rattlesnake jumpy and that rattlers can die of a nervous breakdown."

One rattlesnake, probably the banded, timber, or canebrake, has a sort of immortality. For the Gadsden or South Carolina Rattlesnake Flag shows a coiled snake above the legend "Don't Tread On Me"—a popular slogan during Revolutionary times.

According to sociologists every person should have some sort of hobby to fill in the hours made available by retirement. But probably few will follow in the footsteps of the noted playwright Thornton Wilder. In the spring of 1962 he announced he was looking forward to attracting rattlesnakes to his desert retreat by setting out saucers of milk.

Though a Mr. Alf Evers of Shady, New York, applauded Mr. Wilder's proposed way of life, he took exception to the playwright's intended method of attracting the snakes. Such was his feeling about the matter that he wrote a letter to the *New York Times*, stating that such bait (milk) was "no more attractive to a rattler than a Waldorf salad is to a tiger." Mr. Evers, a self-styled old rattlesnake hand, added:

The supposed craving of rattlesnakes for milk is a widespread bit of snake lore, sprung from a European belief and transferred long ago to the rattler of the New World. In its most usual form the belief is handed on in the folk tale of the little girl who finds an ailing rattler sunning himself on a rock. She brings it a daily saucer of milk and sees it recovering health and strength. The girl's parents become alarmed at their daughter's secret trips from home and follow her to her rendezvous with the rattler. They are horrified and stone the snake, but as the snake's life ebbs so does that of the girl. Both die at sundown.

MOCCASINS
Ancistrodon or *Agkistrodon*

The moccasins, sometimes referred to as "pit vipers without rattles," are represented in the United States by the water moccasin and the copperhead, and in Mexico and countries farther south by the Mexican moccasin. All three snakes are distinguished by somewhat triangular heads covered with large plates, by vertical pupils, and by the telltale pits between eyes and nostrils. The adults are marked by distinct crossbands, and the young usually have bright yellow tail tips.

The water moccasin (*A. piscivorus*) is also known as the cottonmouth because its mouth is lined with white. This pit viper occurs in lowlands from southernmost Virginia to Florida, where its range becomes statewide. From Florida it is found all the way to eastern Texas, and it also occurs in the Mississippi Valley as far north as Illinois and Indiana.

The coloring of the water moccasin helps to identify it and to

Facing page: Cottonmouth, *Ancistrodon piscivorus*

differentiate it from the harmless water snake of the genus *Natrix*. The adult water moccasin is marked with indistinct brown cross-bands on an olive or tan ground, though those in Florida are usually a uniform slaty black. The head is distinguished by a dark top and a dark band on each side. The belly is yellow and splotched with brown or black, with the latter color darkening the underside of the tail.

The young water moccasin, one of a brood of seven to twelve, is much more brightly colored than the adult. The bands are outlined in white, and the tip of the tail is a bright yellow. As the snake matures the colors begin to fade until a half-grown one takes on a greenish or brownish cast, though the bars remain distinct. By the time a moccasin reaches old age, its markings are barely discernible.

Among our poisonous snakes the water moccasin is one of the largest. Though many measure 4 feet, it is not unusual to find specimens 5 feet long. Probably the average length of this heavy, stout-bodied snake is 4½ feet.

The water moccasin frequents low, wet areas, spending many hours draped over a branch of a bush or tree on the bank of a slow-moving waterway. At the slightest indication of danger, it drops from its perch with a plop into the water, and swims beneath the surface to some haven—a stand of reeds or other aquatic emergents.

If the water moccasin cannot escape or is surprised while basking, it draws back its head and opens its mouth wide enough to disclose the white lining—action that may be a prelude to a strike. All during this interlude, the reptile stares fixedly at the intruder. Once in position to strike, it makes its tail quiver as if to say, "Don't you dare come any nearer." Some moccasins strike upon such an occasion but usually most try to get away as quickly as possible after this initial reaction. However, since a moccasin is capable of inflicting a painful wound when it does strike, caution is the watchword in its territory and care is a "must" if a strike is successful.

The water moccasin feeds on a wide variety of other swamp and bog animals. It hunts by day or night, lying hidden in some grassy hummock or floating in the water with most of its body beneath the surface. Thus concealed, it waits for such mammal prey as the young of muskrats, marsh rabbits, and ducks. It also preys on fish of all kinds, and on whatever frogs it can find. In season it "shinnies" up trees in order to devour the eggs of birds and their nestlings. It also eats other snakes, but is reported as not preying on other cottonmouths.

In natural surroundings the water moccasin is considered vicious, but in captivity it appears good-natured because it seems indifferent to everything but food. It does well in captivity, and one is reported as having lived for twenty-one years.

Our other pit viper without rattles is the copperhead or upland moccasin (*A. mokeson*), a hazel-brown snake with hourglass markings on its back. This slender snake, usually measuring 2 to 3 feet, ranges from central Massachusetts to northern Florida, and as far west as Illinois to the north and as eastern Texas to the south.

This moccasin frequents hilly country where there are rocky outcroppings, rock fences, and abandoned stone quarries. It is also found in areas where lumbering operations occurred in times past. In such places there are usually piles of rotting slabs, the discards of the trees that went to market, and the white-footed wood mouse is usually plentiful. A spot like this makes an ideal territory for the copperhead because it furnishes plenty of food, hiding places, and sunning spots. In addition to the wood mouse and other rodents, this pit viper preys upon birds, other snakes—including the garter snake—and frogs and toads.

Each season the female gives birth to a brood of six to twelve—the result of a mating that occurred soon after emerging from hibernation. A young copperhead measures about 10 inches when it is born. By the time it is one hour old, its supply of venom is sufficient to paralyze a mouse. Probably its first food consists of insects in and around the sheltered spot where it was born.

The bright yellow tail tip of a young copperhead is thought to be functional. The snake posts itself at some strategic spot in the litter on the ground, and blends in so well with its surroundings that only the brilliant tail tip is visible. So posted, the young reptile wriggles the tip ever so slightly. Presumably this acts as a lure to entice some bird or other animal to investigate. As soon as it approaches, a strike is forthcoming.

Though the adult copperhead is not normally an aggressive snake, it is one to be reckoned with. Its venom, injected through shorter fangs than those of the rattlesnake, is sufficiently toxic to make anyone extremely ill. And if treatment is not given at once, hospitalization may be necessary. Actually few people are bitten, even though copperheads are found in metropolitan areas, such as greater Washington. Ranger-naturalist J. A. Fowler, of National Capital Parks, writes this about the copperhead in a publication of the National Park Service:

. . . this venomous snake persists within the city proper of Washington [D. C.]. . . . In spite of the occurrence of this snake, only four persons have been bitten in 18 years. None of these cases was fatal.

CORAL SNAKES
Micrurus and *Micruroides*

In Mexico the brightly colored coral snake is known as the "twenty-minute snake." This regional name is applied because the bite of a coral snake is supposed to be fatal within that time. Death from the neurotoxic venom is more likely to occur about twenty-four hours after being bitten. From the somewhat scanty records it appears that about 50 per cent of the bites are fatal.

There are two species of this venomous little reptile in the United States. One is the eastern coral snake, *Micrurus fulvius,* found in lowland country from North Carolina south into and throughout Florida, then west into eastern Texas, and as far north in the Mississippi lowlands as Kentucky. In Mexico it inhabits the provinces of Coahuila and Tamaulipas. The other coral snake (*Micruroides euryxanthus*) is a snake of desert country in Arizona, New Mexico, and northern Mexico.

The bright colors of both species of coral snakes are so similar to those of the scarlet snake and the scarlet king snake, two nonpoisonous species, that it is difficult to tell them apart. A tabulated comparison of the two coral snakes and the two nonpoisonous snakes shows their similarities and differences.

SNAKE	SNOUT	HEAD	RINGS
Scarlet	Red	Sharp, conical	Broad, red and yellow Narrow, black
Scarlet king	Red	Sharp, conical	Broad, red Narrow, yellow and black

SNAKE	SNOUT	HEAD	RINGS
Eastern coral	Black	Blunt, rounded	Broad, red and black Narrow, yellow
Western coral	Black	Blunt, rounded	Broad, red Narrow, yellow and black

The eastern coral snake hatches from a small clutch, usually numbering seven eggs. At the time of hatching it measures about 7½ inches. By the time it is fully grown, it may measure as much as 39 inches, though the average length is about 28 inches. As it matures its colors deepen, the pinkish-red changes to a vivid scarlet, and the black and yellow become more intense.

The coral snake spends much of its time burrowing and in hiding. It comes forth at night or after heavy rains to seek other small snakes, salamanders, and various lizards—including the blue-tailed lizard, of which it seems unduly fond. It probably preys also upon insects and their larvae. It seizes its prey, then injects its venom through short fangs, by repeated chewing until the skin is punctured. The prey is quickly paralyzed, and then ingested at leisure.

The western coral snake, known too as the Sonoran coral snake and the Arizona coral snake, is considerably smaller than the eastern species. It seldom exceeds a length of 18 inches. It is a timid species with a secretive way of life. This may account for the fact that there is no record of anyone's being bitten by this snake in the Southwest.

To complete this roster of poisonous snakes we must include the rear-fanged snakes and can include one of the sea snakes.

The rear-fanged snakes are a mildly venomous group, the Dipsadormorphinae of the Southwest. One representative of this subfamily is the lyre snake, of the genus *Trimorphodon*, so called because there is a dark, lyre-shaped blotch on the head. This rear-fanged species has elliptical pupils, whereas the vine snake of the genus *Oxybelis*, another of the rear-fanged snakes, has eyes in which the pupils are round. None of the lyre or vine snakes are dangerous to man, for their venom is strong enough to paralyze only the smallest mice and the various lizards on which they feed.

The marine species is the yellow-bellied sea snake (*Pelamis platurus*), an ovoviviparous species found in the Gulf of California in the vicinity of Espiritu Santo Island, at the entrance to the Bay of La Paz. This snake and its close relatives seldom bite man except when cornered. But when they do, the bite is usually fatal, for the venom is highly neurotoxic.

Snake Bite and Its Treatment

In January 1958, *Sports Afield* ran an article titled "Experiment In Death," by Harry C. Lewis. This was a picture story with a brief text showing Michigan herpetologist Paul Allen trying to get a 24-inch rattlesnake to strike. The snake did, and struck Allen on the index finger. Then, working in front of a robot camera, Allen and an assistant treated the bite. They used a pocket-sized snake-bite kit (Cutter), a type easily carried by anyone working or vacationing outdoors. This was the procedure for treating the bite:

1. A tourniquet was immediately placed between the bite and the body, as near the fang punctures as possible.
2. Then, thirty seconds later, Allen wrapped a cotton cord around his finger. (Poison and blood oozed from the fang punctures.)
3. The wound was given an antiseptic wash. Next Allen cut around the wound with a scalpel from the kit. (Swelling started at once; it soon became angry-looking and ominous.)
4. The rim of the suction cup was moistened with saliva and clamped over the wound to draw blood and poison. The tourniquet was moved, but not loosened.

For the next two hours, in spite of the prompt treatment, Paul Allen was racked with pain, suffered violent nausea, and succumbed to several fainting spells. He recovered by nightfall, but his arm was swollen for several days after the experiment.

This snake-bite kit, one of several on the market, provides the easiest and quickest form of treatment possible in an outdoor situation, when medical treatment is not available.

Recently the L-C treatment of venomous bites and stings has been revived and publicized. This treatment is a combination of ligature (applying a tourniquet) and cryotherapy (the science or art of healing by means of cold or low temperatures). Unfortunately the L-C treatment has serious drawbacks and, therefore, it is not widely used.

Science News Letter, May 5, 1962, reported on studies of rattlesnake venom at the School of Aerospace Medicine, Brooks Air Force Base, Texas. These studies were carried out under the direction of Dr. William G. Glenn, immunochemist at the school. They indicated that antivenom serums and old-fashioned suction methods for extracting venom are not completely successful. In summarizing his findings for the Federation of American Societies for Experimental Biology, during a meeting at Atlantic City, New Jersey, Dr. Glenn said:

The logical approach to the problem is to study the reasons for the natural immunity in the Florida king snake, the European hedgehog (porcupine) and several other animals. Only the same sort of immunity substance or reaction would be valid protection against snake venom.

Until this immunity substance or reaction is discovered, such standard treatments of snake bite as those provided by the Cutter and other snake-bite kits, or those recommended by the American National Red Cross in its first-aid handbook and in the handbook of the Boy Scouts of America, are the ones to use.

You can help to avoid the danger of snake bite by taking certain precautions. Remember, while walking in snake terrain, to watch where you place your feet; to make sure, while climbing, that your handholds are *not* occupied by sunning snakes; to stand behind stones or logs that you tilt up. Proper clothing for snake country is another way of protecting yourself. Such clothing includes leather boots with loose tops, heavy socks, and trousers worn outside the boots. For trousers, loose and flapping, often cause a snake to strike short.

There is some comfort in knowing the experts believe that more than 75 per cent of all snake bites in this country would not be fatal if given no special treatment. And of course prompt treatment by any of the accepted methods reduces the chance of death from snake bite to perhaps less than 2 per cent for a healthy adult. Finally, it is wise to recall this advice concerning snake bite: DO NOT EXCITE THE VICTIM OR YOURSELF.

HARMLESS SNAKES

Snakes have their place in the balance of nature. In fact,
in some sections of the country blacksnakes are
collected and turned loose to keep down
the rodent population.
DR. MAX HENSLEY
Michigan State University

Dr. Hensley also has this to say about the reptiles in the suborder
Serpentes, "Most aversion to snakes has been passed down from
one generation to another, and many fears are unfounded." How
true this is! I did not overcome my aversion to these reptiles until
I handled a garter snake on the biological preserve at Fredonia
(New York) State Teachers College. Though I had been told
snakes were cool and dry rather than wet and slimy, I did not
actually believe it until I held one in my hand.

The snakes to handle in order "to get the feel of them" are the
smaller nonpoisonous species of Canada, the United States, and
that part of Mexico consisting of the northern and central high-
land. There are at least 116 such species to practice on, with some
form of the striped garter snake readily available in many parts
of temperate North America.

The nonpoisonous snakes of the continent are represented by
two families, Boidae and Colubridae. Of these two families, the
Colubridae, or colubrid snakes, have much the larger representation. They are considered typical nonpoisonous snakes, and are
distinguished for the most part by eyes with round pupils, by the
absence of pits between the eyes and mouth, and by small hooked
teeth but no fangs, except for a few species in the Southwest.
Many give birth to living young. Some are infrequently seen,
whereas others are easily come upon. One in the last category is
the ubiquitous garter snake.

GARTER AND STRIPED SNAKES
Thamnophis

The garter snake so widespread,
Is a snake you need not dread.
Though it's often in the grass,
It never makes a lethal pass
Like the skulking copperhead.

The garter snake is one of the most familiar reptiles of North America. Its range is from southern Canada south throughout the United States and into Central America. It is found from sea level to such altitudes as those of Rocky Mountain National Park, an area of great gorges, lofty peaks, and remote lakes. Here, one form, the greenish mountain garter snake (*Thamnophis elegans elegans*), is the only reptile of the region. Its favorite haunts within the Park's 400 and some square miles are the marshy ponds and slow-moving streams.

Because the mountain garter snake is so partial to water, it is sometimes referred to as a water snake. This liking for water is common to many species and subspecies, including the eastern garter snake (*T. sirtalis sirtalis*). This subspecies ranges from southern Canada to Florida, where it is statewide, and west to Minnesota.

Throughout this extensive range the typical form varies greatly with regard to the livery. The most usual colors are brown, olive, or nearly black. The three stripes are yellowish or greenish, with the central stripe somewhat lighter and broader. Between the stripes are two rows of black spots. The sides are darker than the back, whereas the underside is much lighter. The ridged scales are set in nineteen rows around the slender body; some individuals have only seventeen rows of scales.

Of all our snakes, the garter has the longest active season. It is the first one to come out of hibernation each spring, and also the last to settle down for the winter. It often emerges from some rocky cleft or deep fissure as early as March. Upon leaving its overwintering spot, three or more feet below the surface of the ground, it is ready to warm itself in the early spring sunshine, to seek its first meal, and to look for a mate.

The garter snake usually mates at or near the wintering site. The male has minute sensory organs, little barbels, on his chin. He rubs these along the back of an acquiescent female as his body passes over hers. As a result of this mating, the female brings forth live young late in the summer. The number in a brood varies greatly; sometimes there are only twelve snakelets, though there are records of as many as one hundred. Probably the average litter is fifty or sixty. Only a few from any given litter survive—perhaps Nature's reason for having this snake bear so many.

A young garter snake measures about 6 inches in length at birth. From that moment on, the snakelet has to fend for itself. Its first food is the earthworm, on which it feeds exclusively until it is ready to hibernate for the first time. In the seasons to come, it feeds on such cold-blooded animals as frogs, toads, salamanders, and minnows, as well as upon earthworms—a principal part of its diet. During the first years of its life, it grows about a foot a year. Most of these snakes reach an average length of 36 inches, but the ones in the vicinity of Lake Okeechobee, Florida, measure as much as 44 to 48 inches. By the time the garter snake is two years old it is mature, and during its third spring it is ready to mate.

Each year, as soon as the mating season is over, the garter snakes desert the hibernating area and go to individual home ranges. They establish themselves in ravines similar to the one I knew as a boy (from which they used to glide when the lawn sprinkler was throwing water about); in thickets and grassy meadows; and alongside wet and water areas. One of their haunts in Florida is the Everglades, through which runs the Tamiami Trail. Here, as elsewhere, great numbers of these snakes are killed each year by passing automobiles.

Though the first garter snake I handled did not discharge the contents of its scent glands, it is not unusual for one to do so when frightened or first picked up. The musky-smelling liquid is expelled from two openings near the vent; it is unpleasant but not so overpowering as that of a skunk. A cornered garter snake assumes a defensive position by flattening the head and body, then bites if it can. Its six sets of tiny teeth do little damage, producing no more than faint scratches which soon fade.

A captured garter snake soon becomes tame. A caged specimen glides to the door at feeding time, to take food from your fingers. Such foods are chopped fish and live frogs and toads. And with a cage providing the right environment and food to its liking, a captive may live as long as twelve years.

In the wild the garter snake does not settle down until long after all the other snakes have sought their overwintering spots. One by one the snakes of a region assemble—often gathering on a rocky hill with a southern exposure. During the warmest part of the day they bask in the sun, letting its rays pour down upon their somewhat stiff coils. As the days grow shorter, so do the basking periods. The snakes retreat earlier and earlier to their individual hibernating spots. Finally the day comes when the outside temperature is too low for comfort or safety. This sends the snakes below ground, where they pass the winter in a state of actual suspended animation. Now they are secure against the rigors of winter weather, and will not be seen again until the first suns of spring make it safe for them to emerge in March—the birth month of St. Patrick, the man who is supposed to have rid Ireland of snakes.

Another snake of the same genus as the garter snake is the ribbon snake (*T. sauritus*). This slender species frequents damp terrain in southeastern Canada and the same kind of environment in the United States east of the Mississippi River. It is more aquatic than the garter snake; it swims well and frequently and often dives to the bottom when danger threatens.

The slender body of the ribbon snake is covered with markedly keeled scales; it is black or dark brown on the back, with three vivid yellow stripes. The center stripe is broader than those on the sides and has a ribbonlike appearance—the reason for the common name. The underside is yellow-white and there is a touch of yellow, in the form of a line, beneath each eye. Though some of these snakes grow as long as 3 feet, the more usual length is 2 feet.

In speaking of the ribbon snake, E. Laurence Palmer, Professor of Nature and Science Education, Cornell University, says, "The young and old are usually nervous and resent confinement."

The garter snakes and the ribbon snakes, distinguished by their stripes, are not considered beneficial to man. This is because they eat quantities of cold-blooded animals that include those which aid gardeners and agriculturists. But like all animals they play their roles in various communities by keeping other animal populations under control.

WATER SNAKES
Natrix

According to Carveth Wells, author of *Light on the Dark Continent*, the water snakes of Malaya are undaunted by any obstacles they meet while swimming. On a downstream canoe trip, a 3-foot water snake swimming across the river slid over one side of Wells's boat, slithered across it, and dropped into the water on the other side. Though this is commonplace behavior for the water snakes of Malaya, no one has attributed such actions to any of the eleven species and numerous subspecies of water snakes found in North America.

Among the water snakes in the United States the most widespread is *Natrix sipedon*, the common water snake, also known as the northern banded water snake or the "moccasin." This species is found in lakes, streams, and fresh-water marshes of the eastern half of the country, and in like environments in parts of the central states. Other species and subspecies extend the range south into and throughout Florida and west and south into Lower California.

Common Water Snake,
Natrix sipedon

The heavily keeled scales of a full-grown water snake are light brown or reddish. The back has a pattern of brown bands or splotches, often so large that they obscure most of the basic color. This accounts for the rusty-brown appearance of this snake when it is out of the water. The underside is white or yellow liberally sprinkled with bright red dots, and in some individuals there may be black dots or irregular splotches.

This livery sometimes encases a snake that measures as much as 4 feet. A more average size is 3½ feet, with some 8 inches of tail included in this overall length.

A water snake of this size appears truly formidable when angered or cornered. It flattens its heavy body and wide head as it throws itself forward in a strike. If a strike is successful, its jaws are sufficiently strong to inflict a bite that draws blood. But, contrary to popular belief, this snake cannot inject any venom. For it is a fangless species, and should not be confused with the much stouter water moccasin, whose range overlaps that of *sipedon* in parts of the South.

The water snake is an ovoviviparous species, bearing live young in August or September. Though some species are reported to produce nearly a hundred young, the average litter is twenty-five. At birth the colors of the young snake are much brighter than those of the parents.

The snakelet fends for itself from the moment it is born. It begins a lifetime feeding on such cold-blooded prey as the frogs, toads, and fishes of its environment. The fish on which it preys are the slow-swimming species, not sport fish such as the various trouts. One fish in its diet is the catfish, which it devours without any regard for the fin spines. These frequently pierce the body wall and break off, apparently without doing serious damage.

The common water snake is classed as semiaquatic because it hunts in the water, escapes danger by plopping into it and diving to the bottom, or swims beneath the surface to the protection afforded by a stand of reeds or other aquatic plants. When out of the water, this snake spends many hours draped on the branch of some bush overhanging a stream, pond, or lake. Here it suns itself until danger or hunger causes it to take to the water.

During its active season, when it is out by day or night, the water snake restricts itself to a small home area that it uses year after year. And somewhere within the confines of this small area, it digs in for the winter—frequently a season of hardship for many of the other animals of its community.

Though the common water snake has the widest distribution, it is not the largest of these snakes. It is outmeasured by *N. taxispilota*, the brown water snake, known too as the "water rattler," or the "water pilot." This rusty-brown species attains a length of 5 feet 9 inches, with its long, tapering tail accounting for 12 inches of this overall length.

This snake is found from the Potomac River to the tip of Florida, then west into the lower Mississippi Valley. In the water areas of its range, it brings its tail into play in a peculiar way. It uses the lower part of an aquatic plant as a hitching post by curling its tail around the submerged section. So anchored, the body assumes an almost upright position while the head floats on the surface. Now the snake is in a position to watch its surroundings with its small, bulging eyes—protected by the hard, transparent eyecaps.

Close relatives of these water snakes are the diamond-backed species (*N. rhombifera*), a stout-bodied snake of the lower Mississippi River valley and adjacent areas; the green water snake (*N. cyclopion*), a large, shiny species of the Gulf states; and the flat-tailed or mangrove water snake (*N. s. compressicauda*), a secretive snake confined to southern Florida.

DeKay's Snake or Brown Snake
Storeria dekayi

A number of snakes of differing genera are included in a group known as the brown snakes and the small swamp snakes. One of these is DeKay's snake, a small brown species with large eyes and heavily keeled scales. It is further distinguished by a pale streak down the back, paralleled on either side by a line of black dots. The underside is an unrelieved pinkish white.

DeKay's snake is a species that confines itself to an exceptionally small home range. This may be a pile of rocks, rubble in a vacant lot, or a section of stone fence or wall. Such hideouts may be in any type of locale—urban, suburban, or rural—on a range that includes southern Ontario and most of the United States east of the Rocky Mountains, extending south into Mexico as far as Vera Cruz.

On its range the DeKay's snake is seldom abroad until late in the day. An exception to this usual conduct occurs in early spring, when it spends a part of each day sunning itself on a spot from which it can glide easily and quickly to safety. During the closing hours of the day and all through the night, this small creature seeks a variety of prey. It feeds on earthworms, slugs, the smaller salamanders, and the kinds of beetles that live under rocks.

A DeKay's snake is born alive during August and is one in a litter numbering ten to twenty. At this time it measures no more than 4 inches and its diameter is about $\frac{1}{16}$ inch. The first livery is a dark gray or black, with a white band encircling the neck. These colors are replaced by those of the adult during its first full summer.

As DeKay's snake moves about, it is preyed upon by such birds as hawks and owls, by snake-eating snakes, and by mammal predators such as the skunk and the house cat. Though these predators, and also man, are responsible for killing numberless snakes of this species, it survives and even thrives if given a chance. And therefore it perpetuates the name of James E. DeKay, the early New York zoologist for whom it was named.

FOUR NONCONSTRICTING SNAKES

Diurnal snakes have yellow lenses, the coloring being deepest in species which are swift and sharp-sighted, pale or even lacking in the sluggish and secretive species; nocturnal snakes, on the other hand, all have perfectly colorless lenses.

G. A. BOULENGER,
Catalogue of Snakes, British Museum

Among the North American snakes that are active during the day are the various racers and some other slim, graceful nonconstricting snakes. These diurnal species are represented on this continent by four genera: *Drymarchon, Coluber, Masticophis,* and *Drymobius.* The bodies of these snakes are well designed for what Adolf Portmann calls "the purpose of elementary movements as they are required for nutrition, escape from enemies, defence or for the preservation of the species." Four such snakes, distinguished by eyes with yellow lenses, are presented in this section.

INDIGO SNAKE
Drymarchon corais

The smooth scales of the slender indigo snake are a shiny blue-black. The throat is orange, the chin is orange or white, and the snout and the sides of the head are brownish. This livery encases the largest snake in the United States and Canada. Though the average length is 7 feet, one specimen measured 7 feet 9 inches, including a tail 13½ inches long. And the skin of another measured 11 feet when removed from the body.

The distribution of this lustrous snake is from South Carolina all the way to the tip of Florida and west throughout the Gulf states into Texas as far as the vicinity of the Rio Grande; here it is known as the Texas blue bull snake. On this range the indigo snake favors sandy flats. In such areas, it often seeks safety by gliding into the burrow of a gopher tortoise—a habit which is responsible for the name "gopher snake." It makes a getaway at a speed timed by a stopwatch as 1.18 miles an hour, or perhaps even a little greater if the ground slopes downhill, or when it is being actively chased by a collector.

The indigo snake feeds on a variety of animals. It destroys quantities of rats by overtaking these rodents, pinning them to the ground with a part of its body, and then swallowing them. It also catches other snakes, as well as frogs, toads, lizards, some birds, and an occasional fish. In many areas throughout the South, *D. corais* makes a permanent home near some farm outbuilding, where it keeps the rat population under control. It may live in such a spot for as long as eleven years. This snake hatches from an egg about the size of one laid by a bantam hen.

BLACK RACER ("BLACK SNAKE")
Coluber constrictor constrictor

The *Pennsylvania Game News* once ran a story about a trainer of beagles, a bee tree, and a black snake. While out with his hounds near Meyersdale, Somerset County, in southwestern Pennsylvania, the trainer, Merle Lang, discovered a bee tree. The opening by which the bees were leaving and entering was about twenty feet from the ground. Draped near the opening was a black snake, snapping up bees as they returned from gathering nectar. The snake was knocked from the tree and killed, and when it was opened, it was found to be full of honey bees. The editor of the *News* headed the story "Bees by the Yard." In referring to this bee-eating reptile as a black snake, the *News* editor was using a common name often applied to the black racer.

Though the black racer eats insects, the honey bee is not its usual prey. Abundant throughout its range, this slender, shiny black reptile, with a white throat patch, feeds on a wide variety of animals. These include other snakes, frogs and toads, birds and their eggs, and such rodents as rats, mice, and rabbits. Small animals are swallowed at once, whereas the larger ones are held against the ground as they are ingested.

The range of this racer is from extreme southeastern Canada south throughout the eastern half of the United States—including Florida—and west into Texas. West of the Mississippi, the typical form is replaced by the "blue" racer (*C. constrictor foxi*), a distinct color variety. And in the Far West, from southern British Columbia to the Mexican border, you will find *C. constrictor mormon*, a blue-backed species with a bright yellow belly. Its popular names are the western blue racer or the yellow-bellied racer.

During June or July the female deposits her clutch of white, leathery shelled eggs in some moist spot. This may be under a flat stone, in decaying wood, or in a bank exposed to the sun. A clutch of these elongated, cylindrical eggs numbers five to twenty or possibly a few more. The eggs hatch in four to eight weeks, and the snakelets break out of the shells through narrow slits. The young are about 12 inches in length and have a diameter of ¼ inch.

A young black racer does not look like the offspring of its parents. For it is a pale gray on the upper side, dotted with large brownish patches on the back, and spotted with black on the sides. During the second summer the pattern is much less distinct, and by the third summer, when it measures about 2½ feet, it is a uniform shiny black. By the time it is full grown, it measures nearly 6 feet and has a diameter of more than an inch.

The black racer spends a lot of time sunning at the edge of an open, fairly dry area or draped in the low bushes surrounding such an area. A spot like this affords cover, into which the snake glides at the first sign of danger, and also food in the form of small mice. In such a situation you might chance to capture one of these snakes, though they are adept at getting away.

A cornered or captured black racer is one to be wary of. When one finds no way of escaping, it raises the forward part of its body and launches an upward strike about equal to half its length. It tries to make several successive bites—bites that draw blood if the snake gets its jaws around your hand. Sometimes one of these snakes yanks its jaws sideways as it bites, thus pulling off some skin. As a rule this snake looses its irritability and nervousness after a few weeks of captivity.

EASTERN COACHWHIP SNAKE
Masticophis flagellum flagellum

In *Animal Life and Lore* Osmond P. Breland, Professor of Zoology at the University of Texas, asks: "Does the coachwhip snake whip human beings?" He then answers this question by saying:

In some parts of the United States there is a popular belief that the coachwhip snake will attack a person by wrapping its body around him and administering a sound thrashing with the end of its tail. To add fuel to the story, the color pattern of its tail does resemble a plaited whip. . . . Biologists give no credence to this story.

The slender eastern coachwhip snake is found from the Carolinas south to and throughout Florida, and thence west to the

Rocky Mountains. This narrow-headed snake has dark brown or black scales on the forward portion of the back, a color that becomes lighter toward the rear. The long tail, sometimes measuring as much as a foot and a half, is pale brown. The underside may be white or a clean-looking yellow. There is some variation in color hues and combinations among individuals of this species.

This snake preys on small rodents, birds, and eggs, and perhaps an occasional snake if its usual foods are scarce. Though it goes into trees for some prey, it does most of its hunting in sandy, open country, probably equaling the speed of the red racer ($M. f. piceus$)—reported as 3.6 miles an hour.

The coachwhip is an active, nervous creature, and as a result needs more food than some other snakes. It eats about every five days, consuming several small rodents during one feeding. It presses its prey to the ground, then consumes it head first.

A coachwhip hatches from a clutch consisting of nine to twelve eggs. They are laid on the ground. The crossbanding on a recently hatched snake is three scales in width and is plainly discernible. This fades as the snake matures. Even if captured when young, the coachwhip does not make a good pet. It is extremely nervous and irritable, and if it is annoyed, it vibrates its tail at a furious rate, opens its mouth part way, and raises its head in an attempt to strike.

The western form ($M. f. testaceus$) is known as the prairie racer and the Texas coachwhip snake. It has a great liking for grasshoppers, and consumes them in quantities, as well as eating rodents, birds, and lizards. It preys upon these animals during the day, and has been described as "practically the only desert species that is abroad during the daytime."

Green Spotted or Speckled Racer
Drymobius margaritiferus

The appearance of this snake has been likened to the "handiwork of a Japanese artist in creating a decorative reptile and finishing it with lacquer."

The green spotted or speckled racer completes our roundup of representative racers—regional or widespread. It is a yard-long species distinguished by highly polished dark brown or black scales. The black forms have scales marked in bright green, whereas the brown individuals have spots that are inclined to be yellow. But whatever the color of the spot, there is usually one centered in each scale on the back and the sides.

The spotted or speckled racer's range extends from Panama north into southwestern Texas, as do those of such related species as the ornate racer, the half-striped racer, Schott's racer, and Ruthven's racer—all characterized by great activity and all inclined to nervousness when first captured.

Probably the racers are among the snakes most often associated with the legend: "Should a snake cross the path of a bridal party on their way to church, the union will not be a happy one."

RINGNECK SNAKES
Diadophis

Of the three species of ringneck snakes in North America, the eastern (*D. punctatus*) has the widest distribution. In one form or another you will find this small, retiring, smooth-scaled serpent in southeastern Canada and in most regions of the eastern half of the United States, except for an area in the north central states. Throughout this range the ringneck snake frequents damp, wooded areas, where it passes most of the day secreted under flat rocks or beneath fallen logs.

On the northern part of its range, the color of the back of the ringneck may be slate, brownish, or blue-black. Just behind the head is a narrow band of yellow—the reason for its popular name. The underside is usually a uniform yellow, though some individuals are distinguished by a row of small black dots on the belly.

The ringneck hatches from a small clutch of thin-shelled, elongate eggs. The female deposits them under a flat, sun-warmed rock or in decaying logs during midsummer. The eggs increase in size after they are laid. The period of incubation varies, sometimes lasting as long as two months. As soon as a young snake is fully developed, it breaks the shell of its egg. But it does not leave the safety of the shell at once. It thrusts out its tiny head through a crack to take a look around as if to ascertain whether the area is safe. It may thrust its head out and draw it in several times before finally venturing forth. Once free of its "birth skin," it is a lively little snakelet measuring 3½ to 4 inches in length. Its back is darker than that of an adult, and its "ring of gold" is much brighter than that of an older snake. By the time it is fully grown its overall length is 12 to 20 inches.

The ringneck is seldom seen because it is such a secretive species, coming out from its daytime hiding place only after dark. This is the time it begins its search for prey that includes earthworms, snails, salamanders, and small lizards. It varies this diet by feeding on insects, the young of green and DeKay's snakes, and small frogs such as the wood frog.

The subspecies known as the southern ringneck snake (*D. p. punctatus*) is distinguished by having a belly spotted with black half-moons. This form ranges from southern New Jersey to the Florida Keys. Its back may be brown or black, or of an intermediate color that is a combination of the two. The underside is either yellow or red. Usually such colors are uniform, though in some individuals the red is confined to the rear portion of the belly and the tail.

The southern ringneck sometimes behaves in a manner that has earned it two unusual nicknames. If scared while hunting or routed from its daytime retreat, it raises its tail with a twisting motion that reveals the bright underside. This may well be a defensive measure to scare an intruder into believing the brightly exposed underside is that of a poisonous snake. Such behavior has caused this snake to be known in some areas as the corkscrew snake or thimble snake.

The ringneck snakes in southernmost New Jersey and on the Delmarva Peninsula, the location of Chincoteague National Wildlife Refuge, are neither completely northern nor completely southern in their markings. These snakes are regarded by scientists as intermediate between the northern ringneck snake and the subspecies of the South.

The western ringneck (*D. amabilis*) and various subspecies frequent a narrow range that starts in about the center of the

Pacific Northwest and extends south into northern Mexico. The dark pink neck ring of these snakes matches the underside. A third species (*D. regalis*) lacks the bright neck band of the other ringnecks. This, the largest of all, is found in parts of the Southwest, including the Big Bend country of Texas, and also in northern Mexico.

SMOOTH GREEN SNAKE
Opheodrys vernalis

ROUGH GREEN SNAKE
O. aestivus

Among North American snakes the smooth green snake is undoubtedly the most gentle. Known, too, as the green grass snake, this little reptile has an irregular distribution throughout a range that includes southern Canada from the Maritime Provinces to southern Manitoba, parts of the eastern United States from New England to Florida, and west to North Dakota and Utah and south into Texas and New Mexico.

This little snake with a bright green back and a white or yellowish underside frequents uplands throughout most of its range. In such an environment it is barely distinguishable from the grasses through which it glides with amazing agility. It often coils on some support among a tangle of vines, and unless it moves, blends in so well with its surroundings that it is rarely seen. Sometimes it abandons it usual range to establish itself in some convenient flower garden.

The smooth green snake does not come out of hibernation until late spring, and its active season is not over until late fall—so late that it has been reported as still out and about when there is snow on the ground. Late in the summer the female deposits about a dozen elongate, extremely thin-shelled eggs under a flat stone. She often scoops out a nest under the stone of her choice before expelling her eggs—which are held together in pairs by a gluelike substance. The warmth of the sun on the flat rock helps to incubate the eggs; they hatch toward the end of August, after an interval that may be no more than a few days but never longer than twenty. The snakelet that emerges measures about 4½ inches in length. The scales on its back are dark green, whereas those on the underside are greenish-white. And the scales, as the name implies, are smooth and also have a satiny appearance. In time the dark green is replaced by the light green of the adult, and the underside fades to a uniform white or greenish-white. When it is fully grown, one of these snakes measures about 15 inches, with the tail accounting for about 5 inches of this overall length. Once in a while a specimen measures as much as 2 feet.

The smooth green snake is unusual among snakes because it is insectivorous. It threads its way among the grasses or low plants of its home range, seeking such prey as crickets and grasshoppers, grubs and caterpillars, and some spiders. It has a particular fondness for green, hairless caterpillars that measure no more than an inch. It swallows its prey immediately upon capture. This predilection for insects and their larvae makes the smooth green snake an ally of man in the control of insects.

The rough green snake, distinguished by keeled, divided scales, has a number of vernacular names. Three of these are the green whip snake, the vine snake, and the magnolia snake. But no matter what its vernacular name may be, it is always a uniform light green above and a clean yellow underneath. It frequents a wide variety of habitats from southern New Jersey to the Florida Keys, and west and south to Kansas and Texas. It is also found in Mexico as far south as Tampico.

Wherever you find the rough green snake you will notice that it is active in all the elements of its environment. It climbs well as it forages for insects in brushy tangles or along vine-draped walls and fences. It also glides through the grasses of its own range in search of crickets and grasshoppers, spiders, and the larval forms of moths and butterflies. And from time to time, it seems almost semiaquatic, swimming across any shallow water to get from one spot on its domain to another. It often wriggles along with its pale pink tongue thrust out and held so rigidly that the forked tip is not apparent.

The rough green snake, like the smooth-keeled species, is oviparous. Late in the summer the female deposits her grayish-white, elongate eggs under a flat stone—one that is often near or at the edge of a wooded area. The clutch numbers about a dozen eggs. The moisture of the earthy nest and the sun-warmed rock incubate the eggs in a short time. Probably the period is so short because the embryos are well developed at the time the female expels the eggs. The snakelet that emerges from the eggshell is an emerald green and measures about 5 inches in length. The bright color fades so quickly that the little snake soon resembles its parents.

A full-grown rough green snake is a slender species with a long, tapering tail. Its maximum length may be as much as 36 inches, though a more usual measurement is 30 inches. The length of the tail varies from one foot to a foot and a half, except for those found in the West. The western form (*O. a. majalis*) frequents moist, grassy areas of plains and prairie country. This species is less numerous than it used to be because the drainage of wetlands has destroyed its habitat—habitat that was formerly used by such other wildlife as migratory waterfowl, which are also far less numerous than in years gone by.

The two species of green snakes with the subspecies should be protected. For in their small way, they are allies of man in his constant war against pest insects. As natural or biological controls these snakes do their work without any of the harmful effects of insecticides or pesticides. And to make sure that we always have such controls, their habitats should be left intact or provided.

Unfortunately, in some areas the color of the green snake is thought to be a sign that it is poisonous. So this harmless, beneficial species is frequently killed on sight by those who believe "the only good snake is a dead snake."

HOGNOSE SNAKES
Heterodon

The genus to which these thick-bodied, keeled snakes belong occurs only in North America. The various hognose snakes are serpents of bizarre behavior. When one is disturbed it behaves in a fashion similar to that of the cobras of the Old World. First it dilates the rear of the head and the neck laterally by spreading the long ribs that usually lie against the backbone. This action creates the hooded effect of an angry cobra. At about the same time it is assuming the cobralike appearance, it inhales as deeply as possible. This inflates the stubby body to some extent. Then it exhales so as to produce a long, pronounced hiss. To add to this display of ferocity, it makes repeated strikes in the manner of a copperhead or rattlesnake.

Such a performance is usually enough to frighten the uninitiated. If these tactics do not rout an intruder, the hognose snake takes a second step in what must be considered self-defense. First it opens its mouth, then relaxes until it becomes limp, and lastly rolls over on its back. Now it shudders convulsively, and then after a momentary wriggle of its tail, finally ceases all movement. Now, completely limp from one end to the other, it lies as though dead.

This behavior is nothing more than a sham. For the instant the hognose snake senses that danger no longer threatens, it flips over on its belly and glides off as quickly as possible. However, if it is frightened again, it shams death a second time—a performance that may be executed repeatedly.

The effectiveness of the first maneuver is heightened by the somewhat triangular form of the bluffing snake's head. It also has a thick body and a shovel-like upturned snout—two other physical attributes that also make the hognose snake appear to be dangerous. Consequently it is often regarded with suspicion if not downright fear, for one old wives' tale has it that "a poisonous snake may be told from the harmless ones by a triangular head and thick body."

The hognose snake of the East (*H. platyrhinos*) frequents dry, sandy areas on a range that extends from New Hampshire to south-central Florida and westward to South Dakota, Kansas, and central Texas. It is known by such regional names as "hissing adder," "hissing sand snake," "puff adder," "spreading adder," "flat-headed adder," and "blow viper"—all of which are indicative of the serpent's behavior.

Late in July the female deposits a clutch of leathery white eggs, numbering about twenty. They are expelled in a cluster and adhere

Eastern Hognose Snake,
Heterodon platyrhinos

together. The eggs swell and swell, until just before hatching they have increased in size by about one-third and have taken on a more spherical shape.

Upon hatching a young hognose snake has an overall length of 6 to 8 inches. It is gray, not yellow-brown like an adult, but it does have the same back pattern as its parents. The back is splashed with large patches of black or brown, and on each side is a row of smaller dark patches. Once it attains full growth, it is usually yellow-brown, though there is great color variation among these snakes. Some individuals have a body color that is almost red, whereas others have one that is olive. Occasionally an all-black or gray specimen is reported. The underside is usually yellowish or greenish. The head is likely to be a uniform brown or yellow-brown, and there is a dark band across the head in front of the eyes. Though the record length of one of these snakes is 40 inches, the more usual overall measurement is 18 to 30 inches.

The various hognose snakes frequent a variety of environments. Some are snakes of wooded areas, and are usually much darker in hue than those found elsewhere; others are creatures of dry, sandy areas, and are usually much lighter in color than the average specimen. These snakes also inhabit open fields, frequent the vicinity of swamps, or establish themselves in orchards.

In any one of these environments, the hognose snake glides slowly about in search of prey. So far as anyone knows, it feeds only on frogs and toads, with a strong preference for toads. It seizes its prey, ingesting it head first. A pair of scimitarlike teeth in the back of the mouth help in moving the prey down the throat so that successive swallowing movements finally lodge it where it can be assimilated.

The western hognose snake (*H. nasicus*), distinguished by black on the underside, is a reptile of dry, sandy areas in prairie country. Sometimes known as the "prairie rooter," it is found in Montana and South Dakota and eastward into Iowa, where the range cants off toward the southwest to include parts of Kansas, Texas, and Arizona. The range also extends south of the border as far as central

Western Hognose Snake, *Heterodon nasicus*

Mexico. And there is some evidence that the northernmost limits extend beyond Montana into the Canadian province of Alberta.

The western species has the snout characteristic of all these snakes. The usual length of *H. nasicus* is 16 to 21 inches, with an occasional individual growing as long as 30 inches. And it does not "play dead" as frequently as its eastern relative.

To complete the roster of hognose snakes one must include the dusty (*H. nasicus gloydi*), the plains (*H. n. nasicus*), and the Mexican (*H. n. kennerlyi*), the subspecific members of the genus; and the southern (*H. simus*), the smallest of them all. The range of *H. simus* starts in southeastern North Carolina and ends in south-central Florida to the east and in southern Mississippi to the west.

Another genus includes two species that are similar in appearance to the hognose snakes. These are the hook-nosed snakes (*Ficimia cana* and *F. olivacea*), distinguished by smooth scales and a depression behind the hook on the snout. They are snakes of the Southwest, and the capture of two of them in New Mexico is described in *Copeia* (1931, No. 1, pp. 4–7), by John Van Denburgh:

The male when first found remained motionless, perhaps blinded by the light which I carried; but immediately on being touched it began to writhe and throw its body in strange contortions, as if in agony, sometimes almost throwing itself off the ground. . . . Wright tested the female and found that she reacted in practically the same manner as the male. These tactics were repeated time and again by the two specimens and even when in the collecting sack they continued these strange gyrations and jumping movements . . .

BULL SNAKES
Pituophis

The yellow-headed bull snake is one of our most valuable snakes. For the annual worth of one such snake to agriculturists is said to be about fifteen dollars. The estimate is based on the fact that during its active season it consumes numbers of such crop-destroying rodents as mice, rats, pocket gophers, and ground squirrels. This predilection in food is offset somewhat because the bull snake also devours birds and eggs, ingesting as many as a dozen eggs at one time. The loss of a few birds and some eggs, however, is but small compensation for the good this reptile does.

The range of the bull snake in the United States may be defined roughly as the area between the Mississippi River and the Rocky Mountains. It is also found in southern Alberta and northern Mexico.

In this environment a young bull snake hatches from an egg that is smaller than the average hen's egg and is protected by a tough, creamy-white shell. A clutch consists of twelve to twenty-four eggs that form a single mass because they are stuck together by a gluelike substance. The eggs hatch in eight weeks or so during normal summer temperatures. At hatching time the snakelet is 15 to 20 inches from the tip of its pointed snout to the end of its black-tipped tail.

By the time the bull snake is fully grown its length is usually 5 feet. There are exceptions to this average, for some measure 7 feet, and one established a record length with a measurement of 8 feet 4 inches. Their bodies are yellow-brown, with a row of large, rectangular, black or reddish splotches on the back and similar smaller splotches on the sides. The dark yellow head has a brown or black line across the top, and there are other dark lines from the eyes to the corners of the mouth. Beneath each eye are still other lines. The underside is yellow, and the scales on this part of the body are not keeled.

The bull snake is a noisy species, for it hisses so loudly that it can be heard for at least fifty feet. The hiss is possible because there is an organ known as the epiglottis, a thin lamella of yellow, elastic cartilage, which ordinarily projects upward behind the tongue and just in front of the glottis. When angered the snake inhales deeply; then, with its mouth half open, it exhales, forcing the air against the epiglottis, which vibrates somewhat in the manner of a reed in a wind instrument. The hiss is accompanied by the raising of the body, a forward strike, and a rapid vibration of the tail. Though this behavior is formidable and intimidates anyone unfamiliar with the true disposition of the snake, it is not so dangerous as it appears.

The eastern form of the bull snake is known scientifically as *P. m. melanoleucus*. Its popular names are the pine snake or the white gopher snake, and its range and that of various subspecies is from southern New Jersey south throughout the Atlantic coastal region to the tip of Florida.

The keeled scales on the back of a typical pine snake are dull white, patterned with large black splotches. The white belly is edged by additional black dots, above which are larger dots of the same color. The flattened head is liberally sprinkled with more black spots.

The pine snake hatches from a clutch the female deposits in a nest in a dry pine woods. A clutch contains fifteen to twenty-four eggs; they are incubated by the elements. And from each egg comes

Bull Snake,
Pituophis melanoleucus sayi

a snake that upon full growth is one of the four largest in North America. For the pine snake, a heavy-bodied species, may measure 5 to 8 feet.

The western form of this snake, *P. melanoleucus catenifer*, is known as the Pacific gopher or bull snake. This species has a range that extends from southern British Columbia south and west of the Sierra Nevada all the way into Lower California and other parts of Mexico. The back of this stout-bodied snake is a combination of dull yellow-brown and reddish brown or black patches. The underside is yellow, with a sprinkling of small, dark marks at the edges of the belly plates.

The Pacific gopher or bull snake never attains the length of the related species. Four feet, seven and one-half inches is a good size for one of these species, whose habits are much like those of its close relatives.

All three of these snakes should be protected, because they are among the most effective agents in the control of rodents.

RAT SNAKES
Elaphe

The snakes of this genus are all large, powerful constrictors. They may be identified by their stout bodies and squarish heads, and by bellies so flat as to be almost at right angles to the sides. And the scales of nearly all species are so faintly keeled (ridged) that only close examination reveals that they are not completely smooth.

There are rat snakes both in the Old and in the New World. They are found in tropical as well as in temperate climates. In the New World there are six species and numerous subspecies, that occupy a collective range from southern Ontario to Central America, excepting only Nevada, California, and the extreme Northwest.

One of the many subspecies among these constrictors is the black rat snake (*Elaphe obsoleta obsoleta*), known too as the pilot black-snake, the mountain blacksnake, and the black chicken snake. This member of the group is distinguished by faintly keeled scales on

Black Rat Snake,
Elaphe obsoleta obsoleta

the back, edged in blue-white. This coloring forms a distinct pattern on the back of a juvenile, but as the snake grows older the pattern is much less obvious. The squared head, with its flattened snout, is black, whereas the chin and the throat are pure white. The forward part of the belly is white with splotches of gray—a color that becomes solid toward the rear.

The black rat snake is frequently mistaken for the black racer (*Coluber constrictor constrictor*). Though both are large and black, their differences are apparent when compared on this basis:

BLACK RAT SNAKE		BLACK RACER	
Scales:	keeled, polished	Scales:	smooth, lustrous
Head:	broad, squarish	Head:	narrow
Color:	black, white-edged scales	Color:	black, unrelieved

The distribution of the black rat snake is throughout the greater part of the East from Massachusetts to Florida, then west as far as Michigan, and south into Texas. Throughout this range the black rat snake inhabits a variety of environments. It frequents ravines, river bottoms, hillsides with rocky outcroppings, and beds of disused canals.

During July the female deposits her clutch of twelve to twenty-odd eggs in a nest that may be in sawdust, damp earth, or a manure pile. The thin, leathery shells are coated with a moist, gluelike substance—one that makes the eggs adhere upon drying. As the eggs harden they become slightly yellowed. Upon hatching a young black rat snake has a much more distinct pattern than an adult.

The usual length a black rat snake attains is about 5 feet, though some may be no longer than 3 feet, whereas others measure as much as 6 feet. The record length for one of these snakes is 8 feet 3 inches. The subspecies (*E. o. lindheimeri*) found in Texas is known to reach a length of 7 feet.

Though the black rat snake is a good climber, it does most of its hunting on the ground. It moves slowly over its home range in search of such warm-blooded prey as field and meadow mice, chipmunks and squirrels, and wild and domestic birds and their eggs. Since it is a constrictor, it throws its heavy coils about its victim as

soon as it has been seized. It then ingests its prey. The power of a
black rat snake as a constrictor is such that, when caught, it can
wind around your arm so tightly as to slow circulation to an un-
comfortable degree.

This snake is one about which there is a myth—a myth responsible for the common name "pilot blacksnake." For some reason
superstitious people believed the black rat snake warned such
poisonous snakes as the copperhead and the timber rattler of
danger, then guided them to safety. The myth may have come into
being because the black rat snake frequents areas in which poisonous snakes are found—particularly in the North, where it shares
rocky terrain with these species and from which it glides to safety
when disturbed. Though a poisonous snake of the area may slither
to safety at the same time—hence the myth—it does not always
do so.

The black rat snake is easily caught, but the capturing is often
an unpleasant experience. It is likely to bite and it is sure to excrete
a foul-smelling fluid from glands at the base of the tail. It does tame
to some degree, but as Dr. Ditmars commented, "Captive specimens
cannot be trusted. They are inclined to be nervous and erratic."

Another member of this group is the yellowish-brown corn
snake (*E. guttata*), whose close relatives are the rosy rat snake (*E.
g. rosacea*) and the Great Plains rat snake (*E. g. emoryi*). The
stout-bodied corn snake has such regional names as "red chicken
snake," "mouse snake," and "scarlet racer."

The small-headed corn snake, distinguished by faintly keeled
scales, frequents terrain in which pine barrens predominate.
Though it is most numerous in the southeastern states, you can
find it from southern New Jersey south into and throughout
Florida. The range also extends west into Louisiana and north
throughout the Mississippi Valley as far as Missouri.

During late summer, you are likely to find this reptile in the
vicinity of cornfields. Here it hunts the various rodents that assemble in such areas to feed upon the grain. In early spring it
"shinnies" up trees to feed on birds' eggs and nestlings. Such feeding should be discounted when you consider the numbers of mice,
rats, and rabbits the snake destroys each season, during which its

hunting hours are early morning or late afternoon.

The corn snake hatches from a clutch numbering twelve to twenty-four yellowish-white eggs. Eggs of captive specimens have hatched within six or eight weeks. The eggs of wild snakes, deposited in rotted logs or stumps, probably hatch in about the same time. Upon reaching full growth, one of these snakes occasionally measures as much as 6 feet, but a more usual length is 4 feet, give or take a little.

This colorful member of the rat-snake group spends a part of each year hibernating. In the North it "digs in" deeper and remains inactive longer than in the South, where it overwinters in shallow tunnels burrowed in fields.

Another of these snakes is the yellow rat snake (*E. o. quadrivittata*), variously known as the striped house snake, the chicken snake, the banded chicken snake, and the yellow chicken snake. This snake of many pseudonyms is found in coastal plant and animal communities of the southeastern United States. Throughout this range it is equally at home on the ground or in the trees. It frequently suns itself stretched out on the branch of a live oak, sometimes at heights of twenty to thirty feet above the ground.

The yellow rat snake is oviparous. Before she deposits her eggs, the female often makes a burrow in easily moved soil by pushing it first to one side and then to another. She prepares such a nest in June or July, then deposits about twenty eggs. Each newly laid egg contains a tiny embryo with a thread-thin body and a head so large that it appears oversized in proportion to the body. At the end of three weeks the embryo is well developed, and by the time nine weeks have passed, a snakelet measuring about 12½ inches emerges from the egg.

The average length of a full-grown yellow rat snake is 5 feet. Some specimens are no longer than 3 feet, while still others attain a length of 6 feet. A good-sized specimen is usually bright yellow and marked by four black or dark brown stripes. The stripes on the back are about the width of the row of scales they cover, while those on the sides often cover two rows of scales. Sometimes you find one of these snakes with an olive or pale brown basic color rather than the usual bright yellow. But whatever the color combination this is one of our most handsome constrictors.

Two other members of this group are the eastern and western fox snakes (*E. vulpina gloydi* and *E. v. vulpina*)—snakes of open or wooded country throughout the central states. They have received their common name because they secrete a strong-smelling fluid suggestive of the odor that is noticeable around fox dens or cages. These stout-bodied snakes with keeled scales frequent the vicinity of barns and other farm buildings. For they are great catchers of rats and mice, and are therefore two of our most beneficial snakes.

KING SNAKES
Lampropeltis

One of the largest of the twenty-one nonpoisonous snakes in Great Smoky Mountains National Park is the common king snake (*Lampropeltis getulus*). Here, too, in this primeval, time-worn area you find two other king snakes, the black and the scarlet (*L. g. niger* and *L. doliata doliata*). These are among the rarest snakes in the Park—a mountain wilderness frequented by two of our poisonous snakes, seven of the country's turtles, and eight kinds of lizards.

The common king snake, known, too, as the chain snake and the thunder snake, is a reptile of pine barrens from southern New Jersey to northern Florida. Other species and subspecies extend the range throughout the greater part of the United States, from southern Canada to northern Mexico. Only some of the western and northwestern states south of latitude 40° are excepted from this overall range.

This is one of the largest king snakes, often measuring as much as 6 feet from the front of its small head to the very end of its 8-inch tail. Its color is a shiny black crisscrossed by yellow or white bands that form a chainlike pattern on the sides. The belly is black splotched with white or yellow. And the narrow head, marked with yellow or white, is set off from the stout, cylindrical body by a distinct neck.

If a snake can have a split personality, then this species may be

Common Kingsnake,
Lampropeltis getulus

so described. Apparently it has an affinity for man, for it shows no inclination to attack when its home range is invaded, nor does it attempt to bite when handled; in fact, it coils about a captor's hand and seems to settle down contentedly. On the other hand, it does not live in harmony with its relatives or with other snakes. It does not hunt other snakes, as is frequently reported, but if it runs across one the story is different. It subdues another snake by looping itself around its victim and then applies pressure until the animal is suffocated. A rattlesnake or copperhead does not stand a chance against the common king snake, for this species is not affected by the venom of these pit vipers. As soon as the struggles of its victim cease, it ingests the rattlesnake, rodent, or other prey head first.

The common king snake hatches from a white, leathery-shelled egg—one in a clutch that may number ten to thirty. The female deposits the eggs early in the summer, sometimes laying them on the ground, at other times burying them beneath trash. After all the eggs are expelled, the female may spend the next day coiled around them. The eggs incubate four to six weeks. When the snakelet breaks out of its shell, it measures about 7 to 8 inches and has a color similar to, but brighter than, that of the adult.

In the East the common king snake is subject to intergradation, a merging of one form with another (at the edge of a range) to produce an intermediate form. The king snakes of Georgia,

Alabama, and northern Florida are usually a dull black or dark brown marked with yellow. These snakes mark the intergradation of the common king snake with the Florida king snake (*L. g. floridana*), found from Orange County in east-central Florida to the area of the Miami River.

In the West this group is represented by the California king snake (*L. g. californiae*) of the valleys and mountains of southern California. In the Southwest there is a slate-gray form known as the Davis Mountain king snake (*L. alterna*). It is distinguished by alternating rings of black and red. And it is found only in the vicinity of Davis Mountain in Jeff Davis County near the Mexican border of western Texas.

The scarlet king snake (*L. doliata doliata*) is frequently confused with the poisonous coral snake (see page 22). The narrow bands of this southeastern species are bordered with black and do not encircle the belly. Though the coral snake of the same area looks somewhat like the scarlet king snake, the banding is reversed. Its wide black bands are bordered by narrow yellow bands that encircle the body.

EASTERN MILK SNAKE
Lampropeltis doliata triangulum

The milk snake is supposed to be able to milk cows. Dick Shaffer, editor of *Outdoor Nebraska*, exploded this myth when he wrote:

A snake's mouth is not equipped for sucking in any way. . . . Cows do sometimes suck themselves or each other. Even hogs have been observed doing this. Snakes, however, are not guilty.

One of several milk snakes is the eastern form—a 3-foot reptile that ranges throughout eastern North America from southern Ontario to the Carolinas. It is found in open fields, meadows, and wooded areas. The female deposits six to fifteen oval, white eggs early in July. These are buried in the ground or placed in moist, rotting wood. The eggs hatch during the first part of September. The snakelet that emerges from the broken shell measures 6 to 8 inches in length, and is more brightly marked than the parents.

By the time one of these snakes is fully grown it has an overall length of 34 to 40 inches and a diameter of ⅗ inch. Such a snake is a basic gray on which are superimposed saddles that may be brown, chestnut, or olive. The underside is white, relieved by black dots and splotches. The scales are smooth as satin and have the sheen of this material.

The milk snake is most active during the late afternoon or early evening. During these hours its usual prey consists of rats and mice. It also hunts at night for the spiny lizard, a creature active in its community after the sun has set. And the young of other snakes are also included in its diet. Of this snake's value to the farmer, Percy A. Morris of the Peabody Museum of Natural History writes in *They Hop and Crawl*:

In all likelihood an individual milk snake will destroy three or four times as many mice in a year as an individual owl or hawk, and this in spite of the fact that the reptile takes a vacation every winter for hibernation. Yet, most farmers slay the snakes on sight, while advocating complete protection for the birds.

SOME NOT-SO-FAMILIAR NORTH AMERICAN SNAKES

Among the 250 species and subspecies of North American snakes are a number that are not well known. Many of them are small, harmless snakes restricted to extremely limited ranges. If inked in on a map of North America, some of these ranges would have about the same relation in size to the surrounding countryside as that of a township to a large metropolitan area.

Two of these snakes with restricted ranges are a part of the western fauna. One is the rosy boa (*Lichanura roseofusca*) of southern California and small adjacent areas. Also known as the California boa, this species is a small-scaled constrictor that reaches a length of 3 feet. The names of two subspecies indicate to some degree where to look for them: one is the coastal rosy boa and the other is the desert rosy boa. The other North American boa, a heavy-bodied species, is the rubber boa (*Charina bottae*). This

2-foot, grayish snake is found in the Pacific Northwest, parts of southwestern Canada, and south throughout a narrow inland strip of eastern California. Once again the common names of the subspecies are clues to their whereabouts. They are the Pacific, Rocky Mountain, and southern boas.

Another of these not-so-familiar reptiles is the slender blind snake belonging to the genus *Leptotyphlops*. These truly blind snakes of the Southwest, and those of the genus *Typhlops* in Mexico, are the only serpents in North America without large abdominal scales. They are wormlike in both color and circumference, and seldom grow much longer than 8 or 12 inches. They are burrowers, and though they feed on some larval insect forms and earthworms, the greater part of their diet is adult termites.

On the other side of the continent is the rainbow snake (*Abastor erythrogrammus*), a colorful reptile of swampy areas in the Gulf states and in similar areas along the Atlantic coast as far north as Virginia. This is a burrowing snake related to the mud snake (*Farancia abacura*), another burrowing species of much the same distribution. The rainbow snake, distinguished by red or orange stripes, is the smaller of the two. It attains a maximum length of 3 feet 4 inches, whereas the mud snake has an overall length that varies from 4 to 6 feet. Before shedding, the skins of these smooth-scaled snakes become a translucent blue.

Two other snakes with restricted ranges are the sharp-tailed snake (*Contia tenuis*), found in a coastal strip of the Pacific Northwest, and the striped swamp snake (*Liodytes alleni*) of southern Georgia and most of Florida. One subspecies of the genus *Liodytes* is the Everglades swamp snake, a semiaquatic form that feeds on frogs and crayfish. It is a shiny brown, smooth-scaled species with a yellow underside.

Texas has a snake whose popular name is the same as that of the state in which you find it. This is the Texas cat-eyed snake, a subspecies known scientifically as *Leptodeira septentrionalis septentrionalis*. It has large eyes in which the pupils are vertically elliptical, a slender body, yellowish or gray-green above and yellow below, and a tapered tail ending in a slender tip. It is a nocturnal creature that frequents home ranges in southern Texas and in Mexico to Veracruz As a captive it feeds on small mice and frogs as well as lizards. Probably in the wild it hunts just such prey as it slithers across empty stretches of country in southern-most Texas.

The yellow-lipped snake (*Rhadinaea flavilata*) is a smooth-scaled serpent whose popular name derives from the fact that its upper lip is a bright yellow. It is so rare that it is seldom seen on a range along the Atlantic coast from North Carolina to Florida and inland to Mississippi. Though *flavilata* sometimes attains a length of 15 inches, it is usually no longer than 10 or 12 inches. It feeds on other snakes and lizards and also on frogs and toads. Another snake in this group is also rare. This is the short-tailed snake (*Stilosoma extenuatum*) that attains a length of 8 to 24 inches, with the tail accounting for little more than 2 inches of this overall measurement. It is a burrowing species confined to the pine woods of three counties in central Florida. Of this snake A. F. Carr, Jr., Department of Biology at the University of Florida, once wrote:

When handled, although alert, it seems quite unafraid, and if treated roughly it becomes enraged, coiling, vibrating its meager tail and strik-ing like an irate blacksnake.

Its powers of constriction and muscular control are remarkable. When it coils about my first and second fingers, I find it impossible to part them. . . .

The Texas long-nosed snake (*Rhinocheilus lecontei tessellatus*) inhabits, of course, the state from which it gets its common name. This is a smooth-scaled snake distinguished by a snout that may be red or pink and that is definitely upturned and pointed. Its color combination of black, red, and yellow is seldom seen, for it slithers across deserts and prairies at night as it hunts for lizards and their eggs, insects, and small rodents. Within this area are some of the tiny black-headed snakes (*Tantilla*). One such is the Texas black-headed snake (*Tantilla nigriceps fumiceps*), whose head is crowned with a cap of black scales. This snake and its close allies are small and secretive, hiding by day and hunting by night.

An exception among the snakes classified as black-headed is

T. gracilis. The common name of this species is the flat-headed snake. And the reason it is an exception is that it does not have the usual black cap or crown. Its head is generally somewhat darker than the basic color—brown, gray-brown, or golden-brown.

The atypical flat-headed snake is the last of our not-so-familiar snakes. These snakes and the others described in this book are but a partial representation of the North American snakes. Like any other form of wildlife, they have their place in their respective communities. As Roger Conant writes in *A Field Guide to Reptiles and Amphibians of Eastern North America:*

Even herptiles [reptiles and amphibians] have a place in the balance of nature. . . . And the value of snakes in destroying rodents has long been recognized.

LIZARDS

> . . . And the green lizard, and the golden snake,
> Like unimprisoned flames, out of their trance awake.
> SHELLEY, *Adonais*

One of the world's famous fictional animals is "Little Bill," the lizard in *Alice in Wonderland* who made a jack-in-the-box exit from the chimney of "a neat little house, owned by W. Rabbit." The force that launched Little Bill skyward was a kick administered by Alice herself, during the interval when she had grown so large she could not get out of the White Rabbit's house.

In one edition of *Alice*, Little Bill has a greenish cast with slight golden overtones. Since some lizards are capable of remarkable color changes, perhaps this tinting by Fritz Kredel of the Tenniel illustration is not exaggerated.

Little Bill and all his kind belong to a suborder of reptiles named Sauria, the saurians. This is the largest group among reptiles; it is represented throughout the world by more than 3,000 species. Most of today's lizards might be called diminutive when compared to their ancestors of prehistoric times. These ancestors, evolving independently from the "stem reptiles" known as Cotylosaurs, along with many other creatures of their kind dominated the earth to such an extent that we had what is known as the Age of Reptiles. Most of these reptiles vanished at the close of the Mesozoic era. The end of this era ushered in the Cenozoic, an interval that is a time bridge from the Age of Reptiles to the present.

In our time the best place to get some conception of the lizard world of yesterday is the Galápagos Islands—a volcanic group 650 miles off the west coast of Ecuador. Here, as at the time of

Charles Darwin's visit in 1853, you can glimpse the past on an archipelago which the Spaniards named *Las Islas Encantadas* ("the enchanted isles") some years after their discovery in 1553.

Today the Galápagos seem truly enchanted, for on them you can see creatures that have been arrested in various stages of evolution—"living fossils," as these animals were designated by Darwin. Some of the animals on the Galápagos seem like the dragons of mythology. Two such are iguanas—lizards that resemble their forebears on earth during the Age of Reptiles.

One Galápagos dragon is the sea iguana, a crested lizard measuring 3 feet in length and weighing twenty pounds. These gray-black reptiles, called "imps of darkness" by Darwin, appear ferocious. But they are mild creatures, feeding on algae and seaweeds—exposed at low tide on offshore rocks and periodically covered again by the cool waters of the Humboldt Current.

The second dragon, the land iguana, is a large, sluggish reptile whose skin has a greenish cast. Like the sea iguana, it is a vegetarian. Usually it feeds on the ground, but from time to time it clambers into the low and stunted acacias to browse on the leaves of these tropical and subtropical trees.

Another reptile found throughout these burning hot, nearly rainless islands is the lava lizard. This mottled, slant-eyed animal is one of the area's cannibals, for it preys on the smaller members of its family.

These lizards, and such other animals as the scarlet rock crab, the Galápagos snake that preys on the lava lizard, and the flightless cormorant, are members of a strange plant and animal community brought into being by a combination of cool waters and equatorial suns. Some of these eerie animals, such as the lava lizard, are found throughout the Islands, but others are restricted to Narborough—a spray-washed circle of lava dominated by an active volcano in its center.

The cliffs of Narborough and the other Enchanted Isles, dotted with prickly pear cacti and alive with what seem to be antique animals, were fittingly described by the master of the *Beagle*, the ship that brought Darwin to the Galápagos September 15, 1853. Captain Fitz-Roy called these cliffs "a fit shore for Pandemonium."

Now the Enchanted Isles of the Spaniards are a wildlife sanctuary, one of the very few places that preserve a fauna long since extinct in other parts of the world. The animals of the Galápagos canvas are a fascinating study, but one limited to a few because the Isles are so remote. But, fortunately, a general study of lizards need not be confined to these Islands, for there are lizards in other, more easily reached parts of the world.

Though no lizards today match the size or equal the ferocity of some of their ancestors, there is still a great variation among these long-bodied creatures. Some, such as the noisy geckos, are only an inch or so in length; others, like the Komodo dragons of three Malayan islands, measure as much as 12 feet from tip of snout to tip of tail. And most of them favor the sun and avoid water, except for *Amblyrhynchus*, the marine lizard that frequents the rocky shores of the Galápagos Islands, feeding on seaweeds.

The other physical characteristics of these reptiles also differ greatly. Some have short legs; others have only remnants; and still others are legless. Lizards are further distinguished by eye coverings, either movable or fixed; usually a sign of an external ear; and tongues that may be either short and only slightly forked or long and deeply forked. And most lizards have the ability to grow a new tail to replace one that is lost.

In North America there are more families of lizards than there are families of snakes. The nine families of lizards here account for nearly eighty species in Canada and the United States, and in Mexico there are at least 270 kinds. Some of these lizards are found in all three countries. And Canada has no species that are unique, for all distributions of all the lizards in this country extend southward into the United States.

Our various lizards are found, for the most part, in three types of habitat. Some are arboreal, spending the better part of their lives above ground; others are strictly terrestrial, confining their activities to the ground; and still others are largely subterrestrial, with most activity devoted to burrowing and tunneling. These animals of high and low life have diversified diets. They may be herbivorous, insectivorous, omnivorous, or carnivorous. And the carnivorous species include some that are cannibals. Most North American lizards are insect-eaters, and as such are considered highly beneficial.

In Utah, for instance, the lizard is a natural control of the beet leafhopper—an insect that is the only known carrier of "curly top." This is a destructive virus disease that affects sugar beets, table crops, and many flowering ornamental plants. In Ceylon, one of the monitors (*Varanus salvator*) preys on crabs. This predilection is fortunate, for the crabs destroy the banks of rice fields on this island. In recognition of the monitor's worth to the rice growers, the animal is protected by law. And in Ceylon and elsewhere the monitor lizards are valuable members of plant and animal communities because they feed on rats.

The distribution of the lizards in North America is not so extensive as that of the continent's snakes. No lizard is found as far north as the area around the southern end of Hudson Bay, nor are there any in the northern parts of New England. In the East as a whole there are few lizards, whereas in the hot, dry regions of the Southwest these scaled reptiles are numerous.

Some lizards indulge in a habit little practiced by snakes. This is island-hopping. Through the years they have extended their ranges to include many islands of the central and south Pacific. One island group which lizards have made their territory is that covered by the state of Hawaii. The lizards of North America are:

Geckos (Gekkonidae)
Iguanas, chuckwallas, desert lizards, horned toads, spiny lizards
  (Iguanidae)
Glass snakes, plated lizards (Anguidae)
Limbless lizards (Anniellidae)
Beaded lizards (Helodermatidae)
Xantusiids (Xantusidae)
Teids or striped lizards, also called racerunners (Teiidae)
Skinks (Scincidae)
Worm lizards (Amphisbaenidae)

GECKOS
Gekkonidae

The geckos are represented in the United States by at least three native species, and possibly a fourth. For there is one whose status is still uncertain. One native species is found in a small area where Mexico and California meet. This is the Mexican leaf-fingered or leaf-toed gecko (*Phyllodactylus tuberculosus*), a creature whose color combinations are suited to the dry and rocky country in which it lives. Its basic color may be light yellow-brown, pale red, pale gray, or pale brown, spotted with dark brown or slate gray.

The name of this lizard refers to its well-developed toe pads, which are leaflike in appearance. These pads are also extremely functional because the undersides are equipped with spongy, adhesive disks. So equipped, the gecko is able to scamper over smooth or vertical surfaces in pursuit of insect prey—which it frequently hunts in the huts of Indians living in this barren country. A creature of the night, the Mexican leaf-toed or leaf-fingered gecko is distinguished by large eyes in which the pupils are elliptical.

A second native species in the United States is the banded gecko (*Coleonyx variegatus*). Like all other geckos, it has a voice, emitting little chirps as it scurries from one clump of cactus to another in the desert, or as it scrambles over rock in other parts of its range. This is in Arizona, California, New Mexico, and Texas and on several islands in the Gulf of California.

The banded gecko, measuring about 5 inches in length, is a slender, large-headed lizard with a somewhat short and sturdy tail. Its basic body color is yellow or yellow-white relieved by several bands of chestnut brown. The bands on the body do not make complete circles, but end on the sides. Those on the tail, however, are complete; they encircle this appendage so there are alternating rings of light and dark. One form, or race, is known as the spotted gecko because the bands are indistinct or obscured by splotches of color.

By day the banded gecko secretes itself in a rocky crevice or rodent burrow; by night, after emerging about dusk, it stalks insect prey. It moves slowly and deliberately on padless toes, and with its almost catlike eyes opened wide so the lids do not interfere at all with its vision. A hunting gecko upon reaching its prey moves in with a rush to seize and hold it with its jaws. In turn this gecko is preyed upon by the larger lizards and also by the snakes of the area.

The male banded gecko is given to fighting with other males. One in fighting form rises as high as possible on his somewhat bowed legs, arches his back, and fans out the folds of skin at his throat. This fighting form is further augmented by lowering his large, flattish head. Once this stance is assumed, the aggressor circles his opponent, pausing to bump him whenever possible and wherever possible. The fighting ends when the aggressor routs the enemy with a bite.

Courtship is an equally active affair. The male lowers his body, points his snout toward the ground, and moves in to the female, with his 2½-inch tail waving. Sometimes he pokes the female with his

Banded Gecko, *Coleonyx variegatus;*
crossing white line on highway

little snout; at other times he licks her with his tongue. Once these preliminaries have been executed, the male nips the female on the body, then follows this action by gripping her on the neck or shoulders as a prelude to the actual mating.

During the summer the female lays one or two small, white, brittle-shelled eggs. They are coated with a sticky substance that makes them adhere to whatever spot the female chooses for their disposition. Egg-laying and all other gecko activity is carried on during the night. Because this activity is nocturnal, the details of this lizard's life history and behavior are incomplete.

Other geckos in the United States are exotics, having been brought to this country in the holds of ships. In Florida and on the nearby Keys, you find such Old World species as the Mediterranean gecko (*Hemidactylus turcicus*), one of the house geckos—a small gray or brown creature covered with predominantly fine scales.

A second gecko that has become established in southernmost Florida and on some of the smaller Keys is a dwarf species. This is the reef gecko (*Sphaerodactylus notatus*)—possibly the smallest reptile in the country. For it measures only 2⅝ inches in overall length.

The geckos native to the United States, and the introduced species, are the only representatives we have of a family that numbers four hundred. The family name derives from the call of an Old World species, the tokay, whose scientific name is *Gekko gecko*. The tokay is the largest member of the family, sometimes reaching a length of 14 inches. And the smallest member of the family is a West Indian species (*Sphaerodactylus elegans*). As an adult, it measures 1.3 inches in length.

AMERICAN CHAMELEON or ANOLE
Anolis carolinensis

In *Animal Forms and Patterns*, Adolf Portmann states, "The instrument of colour play is attuned to a variety of functions. . . . The colour display of the American *Anolis*, too, is very dramatic; its lively temperament exhibits anger and fright; and this, as well as the transition from nocturnal rest to active life in the sun, may be revealed by a change in the colour of its coat."

Though the American chameleon or anole does undergo color changes, it is not a true chameleon. It lacks the prehensile tail that is a distinguishing characteristic of the true chameleon—a species confined to the Old World. Our "chameleon," a tiny-scaled creature, is a common lizard of southeastern coastal regions, with a range from North Carolina to Florida, and then west into Texas.

Throughout its range the anole is known by its popular name "chameleon" as well as such other names as "fence lizard" and "green lizard." But no matter what you call it, it is an unusual lizard because it has the ability to change color. Usually *Anolis* is pale green, but when it is excited or combative it becomes a brilliant emerald. At rest, its color is generally brown or dark gray. Surroundings have little influence on the anole's color, for you will sometimes see a brown individual among the greenest of leaves, or a bright green one scrambling over a gray rock.

In its daily hunting, the anole searches for such insect prey as beetles, butterflies, gnats, and wasps, as well as scorpions and spiders. A hunting anole hugs the branch on which it spots its prey. It moves along at a slow, cautious crawl; then, as it rushes in for the kill, it opens its mouth wide enough to snap up the prey. If the victim is small, the anole swallows it whole; if it is large, the lizard chops it up with its sharp teeth before gulping it down. The anole also enters houses in pursuit of prey. As it stalks flies and mosquitoes, it scurries over walls and ceilings, held in place by the adhesive pads on its tiny feet. As it hunts, the anole uses its eyes to the best possible advantage. The eyes, set in little turretlike processes, are independent of one another; thus the anole can follow the movements of prey with one eye, while looking elsewhere with the other.

An adult anole has the appearance of a miniature dragon. At its greatest length, one of these lizards measures no more than 7 inches. The body is covered with minute scales, while the head is adorned with a tiny crest. There is a small dewlap at the throat. This fold of skin seems to be purposeless in the female, but in the male this crimson throat fan flares out during courtship or at times of combat.

An anole in active combat is a bright green, with the dewlap flared and the crest raised. At times a fighting anole displays a black spot behind each eye. Snapping its sharp little teeth, one male lunges at another in the arena where the fight occurs—a small section of a tree limb. The two lock in combat until one or the other loses his long, tapering tail. The victor sometimes marches off with the tail of the vanquished held between his jaws. The loser of the fight, and of the tail, has the ability to grow a new one. The second tail is never a perfect replacement, for there is usually a slight bump where the new growth started.

The courtship antics of the male anole begin with the establishment of a very definite territory. He defends it against all other males who come a-courting. When a male finally drives any intruder from his territory, he then approaches the female in a manner best described as a strut. The female acquiesces by dropping her head low, and shortly thereafter a mating takes place.

As a rule the tiny eggs are deposited one at a time, at intervals of two weeks throughout the late spring and early summer. The laying span depends upon the whereabouts of the female on the range. The eggs are laid in moist debris and hatch in about six weeks. The young, miniatures of the parents, stay in seclusion until they can fend for themselves. They get no parental care during this period of hiding. Within a few days after hatching, they start hunting on their own. A female grows more rapidly than a male, and also matures more rapidly. The life span of this lizard is probably two years, with an exceptional individual living as long as three years.

The anole frequenting Key West is known scientifically as *Anolis sagrei stejnegeri*. This rare subspecies (the Key West anole) is named in honor of Dr. Leonard Stejneger, one of America's outstanding herpetologists. It is so rare that it was probably never captured to be sold at country fairs, circuses, and carnivals as was *A. carolinensis*. Today the sale of the American "chameleon" is prohibited by law—which is good. For vendors took little care of the lizards offered for sale and most purchasers did not know how to care for their pets.

CHUCKWALLA OR CHUCKAWALLA
Sauromalus obesus

One of the plants of the Southwest is the flat-leaved prickly pear —a cactus with large, spectacular yellow flowers. One of the animals native to areas where this cactus blooms in the spring is the chuckwalla or chuckawalla, a chunky lizard that eats flowers. Though it feeds on blossoms of all colors, the chuckwalla seemingly has a particular liking for those that are yellow. It nibbles away at such flowers with slow deliberation, as if relishing every mouthful. It also eats the fruits of various plants, including those of the yellow-flowered, low-growing Engelmann's pear cactus—fruits that are mahogany in color and are known as "tunas" when fully ripe.

This Ferdinand of the saurian world is our second largest lizard, a harmless reptile ranking in weight immediately below the poisonous Gila monster. An unusually large chuckwalla attains a length of 18 inches and weighs as much as three or four pounds. A more usual size is 10 or 12 inches, with a weight to correspond. But short or long, the chuckwalla is a plump creature that is well described by its specific scientific name *obesus*.

During the day the blackish-white or somewhat reddish chuckwalla is out on a range that extends from southernmost Utah and Nevada south into northern Mexico. Other races or forms are found along a narrow strip bordering the Gulf of California. As one of these lizards moves about, it flicks its tongue out and in to carry particles to its organs of smell—a way perhaps of sampling food.

A chuckwalla often feeds early in the morning and again in the evening. Between its morning and evening meals, it spends a great deal of time sunning itself on any convenient rock among those that dot the dry slopes of its home range. If alarmed it hustles into a nearby crevice. As soon as it is secreted, the chuckwalla inflates its lungs until the body swells to a size 50 or even 60 per cent greater than normal. So enlarged, this lizard is impossible to haul out of its rocky fastness.

The Indians used to consider the chuckwalla a great delicacy. They caught it by thrusting a sharply pointed stick into the crevice in order to puncture the animal's lungs. As soon as the body deflated, the chuckwalla was pulled out. Enemies other than man that cause the chuckwalla to run for its life are the gray or gray-brown coyote and the large-eared kit fox. Various birds of the community prey on it also, and the shadow of the turkey vulture, an eater of carrion, sends the chuckwalla scurrying to seek safety in some rocky crevice.

Not much is known about the life history of this lizard, but it is thought to be one that reproduces by laying eggs. You can tell young chuckwallas by the bands across both body and tail, whereas some adults have bands only on the tail and still others have no bands at all.

Occasionally the chunky chuckwalla is referred to as the "alderman lizard," perhaps because its coloring is subdued and its movements are deliberate. Its popular name is probably American Indian in origin.

Desert Iguana or Crested Lizard
Dipsosaurus dorsalis

The hottest of the North American deserts is undoubtedly the Mojave in southern California and Nevada. This is a land of cactus plants and yuccas, Joshua and smoke trees, and the creosote bush. It is also the land of the desert iguana or crested lizard, a saurian that is capable of enduring the greatest body heat of all the desert reptiles. For it is out and about when the thermometer registers 115.5° F.

This lizard, measuring 10 to 12 inches, has a cream-colored body marked with brown, reddish-brown, or black lines and spots. The lines run lengthwise along the body, with the dots interspersed. The head is rather small, the body is stocky, and the tail, long and tapering, is almost twice the length of the body. From the nape of the neck to nearly the end of the tail is a single row of larger scales. These are similar to the dorsal fringe of the true iguanas. This is the only lizard in the United States with such a crest or fringe.

In the spring the desert iguana moves over the desert floor in search of its favorite seasonal food, the creosote bush—a widespread, yellow-flowering plant of the Sonoran Zone. When this bush's season of bloom is over, the desert iguana eats other flowers. But as summer progresses, there is no vegetation that seems to appeal to its palate, and a diet of desert insects and even some carrion is substituted.

This lizard is a swift-moving species. It runs with surprising speed, frequently rising up on its hind legs as it scampers over its sandy home range. Running upright—known as bipedal locomotion —is accomplished with the tail wavering for balance, and the forelegs held close to the body. A lizard running in this position looks like some tiny dinosaur. For *Tyrannosaurus*, greatest of all land-living predators, ran in the same way. If you manage to catch one of these lizards by the tail, it turns quickly and the tail breaks off at the joint, from which a new, less perfect one grows in time.

Like all other lizards, with the exception of a small uta, the desert iguana hibernates for brief intervals. During its active period, it uses some mammal's burrow for its home or digs a retreat of its own. And during its active period the female lays her eggs, and in a matter of weeks the young hatch to produce a new generation of our most heat-tolerant desert reptile.

COLLARED LIZARD
Crotaphytus collaris

LEOPARD LIZARD
C. wislizeni

After two days and two nights of continuous travel over a waste of alkali and sand, we were still surrounded as far as the eye could see by a region of fearful desolation.

This is the way in which Elizabeth Donner Houghton wrote of the Great Basin Desert, through which she passed on her way to California in 1846. In this "region of fearful desolation" the lizards are represented by several species. One of these is the collared lizard, a stout-bodied saurian that runs on its hind legs when frightened.

It starts running on all four legs, rears up, then takes off over the desert floor on its long, strong hind legs. It races over the sand, using its slender, tapering tail to maintain balance in the way a wire-walker uses a pole. From time to time it makes kangaroo-like leaps to bridge any depressions in its course. Frequently one of these lizards runs upright for ten or more feet, and so swift is its passing that an adult can outdistance many predators.

The most striking physical aspect of this Great Basin lizard is a part of its livery. Two bands of black enclosing one of white circle the neck to make a collar. This separates the large brown head from the short, stocky body. Usually the body is green, though it may be yellow-white or even a pale gray. But no matter the color, there is always a sprinkling of white dots. The underside is bright green, while the throat patch is orange. The female is less brilliantly colored, though her postnuptial—after the eggs are fertilized—appearance is arresting. For now her body is marked by a series of bright red spots. Old collared lizards often appear to be faded, with only the black retaining its intensity.

Mating takes place early in the summer, and some two weeks later the female is ready to lay her eggs. They are covered by a paper-thin material and measure about ⅜ inch in length. A clutch, numbering four to twenty-four, hatches in nine weeks. A little collared lizard breaks out of its shell at about the time people are preparing for the Labor Day weekend.

The baby collared lizard works its way to the surface from a depth of about 5 inches. When one emerges from the sand, it is black in color and measures no more than 1½ inches from end to end.

In the year of its hatching, a collared lizard is active only for a few weeks. For the time of hibernation is at hand. It passes this interval deep in some rocky crevice. One of these lizards has to hibernate a second time before it reaches full size—a total length of 10 to 12 inches, with the tail accounting for more than half that length. And the hind legs will be nearly three times as long as the short, froglike front ones.

The collared lizard is active during the day on a home range that is dry and open, and one that has plenty of rocky outcroppings. A rock serves as a point of vantage and a place to sun. This passive interlude in the day occurs when the temperature of the air is 71°–91° F. and that of the lizard's body nearly 100° F. From time to time the collared lizard interrupts its sunning to search for live prey. This includes other smaller, more slender lizards, snakes such as juvenile striped racers, and various insects including the grasshopper and the cricket. On occasion it devours a young spiny horned lizard. It also eats the tender leaves and blossoms of low-growing plants. One of these is the oval-leaved shadscale or sheep fat—a desert growth that is an important forage plant for livestock.

As it moves about on its home range, the collared lizard has to be wary of various birds, including the long-legged roadrunner, that can race along at twenty-two miles an hour. Fully grown snakes of the area are predators, too. Most of the collared lizards caught by predators either are immature or females digging their saucer-like nests.

On overcast days the collared lizard is seldom active, and is therefore safe from most of its predators. And by sunset it is holed up somewhere on its home range in this region of fearful desolation.

Throughout the sandy open regions of North America's desert country, you will find a lizard with dark brown spots on the back and upper surfaces of the legs. This is the leopard lizard, measuring from 12 to 16 inches, and further distinguished by a white throat and belly, gray upper parts, and light bands on the back. It also has a long, tapering tail.

This lizard is out by day, hunting live prey that includes all sorts of insects, small snakes, and other lizards, some of which are its own kind. Occasionally it starts to ingest prey that is too large for easy swallowing. As a result the lizard is liable to be the victim of its own greed, and to die while trying to get down its meal.

Neither the collared nor the leopard lizard makes a good pet, for both are inclined to bite when captured. Of the collared lizard, Raymond L. Ditmars once wrote: "The jaws are strong enough to produce a fair blister upon one's finger."

ROCK, TREE, and SIDE-BLOTCHED LIZARDS
Petrosaurus, Urosaurus, Uta

Formerly these lizards were known as "swifts," a term now avoided because it is used to designate certain birds and mammals.

Leopard Lizard,
Crotaphytus wislizeni

And once, too, these lizards were all in one genus, *Uta*, but now they have been partitioned into three different genera, represented in the United States by species living in greatly varied habitats, including islands in the Gulf of California.

One representative member of this group is the small-scaled side-blotched lizard (*Uta stansburiana*), whose livery may be dark green, gray, brownish, or purplish. It is a reptile of arid regions from below sea level to altitudes of seven thousand feet. In the warmer parts of its range, this little lizard is active all year round, scuttling through sagebrush or scampering over rocks in search of prey.

Sometimes called the brown-shouldered lizard, *U. stansburiana* is a small, finely scaled creature seldom measuring more than 4 inches from the tip of its blunted snout to the end of its long tail. Though the male is distinguished by pale blue patches on the undersides near the hind legs, the female has no such coloring.

The side-blotched uta has the widest distribution of all the members of this group. Its range extends from the Southwest as far north as Washington. It is a strictly terrestrial species. It runs down prey, or escapes predators, by racing along so rapidly that it appears to skim over the ground. It does not, so far as is known, ever rear up on its bowed hind legs as do some of the other lizards. It is nearly impossible to catch one during the day, but at night—a less active period—capture is possible.

Close relatives of the utas in the United States include the climbing or tree lizards of the genus *Urosaurus*. One inhabits western Texas, Utah, Nevada, and California. Measuring about 6 inches, it is gray and banded with black. The male has a large blue patch on each side of the abdomen—a mark not found in the female.

This reptile, perfectly at home on the ground, seems to prefer climbing the sheer sides of rocks and boulders or scampering up and down the branches of trees and bushes. It does not have adhesive pads or disks on its feet like the geckos, but is able to maintain a foothold because it has long, strong, sharp claws that dig in.

The largest of this group in the United States is the banded rock lizard (*Streptosaurus mearnsi*). This species, with a jet-black band across the shoulders, grows to a length of 11 inches. It is found in the rocky terrain of southern California and Baja California.

From the largest to the smallest, the lizards of this group in the United States are egg-laying species—species that belong to a dominant family in the New World.

EASTERN FENCE LIZARD
Sceloporus undulatus

Although most of our thirty-odd spiny lizards are creatures of high, dry areas in the Southwest, there are a few exceptions to the usual whereabouts of these reptiles. One of these exceptions is the eastern fence lizard, numerous in the East from southernmost New York to Florida. Throughout this range its preferred habitat seems to be pinewoods areas or regions where there were recent lumbering operations.

The eastern fence lizard is one of the smaller species in this group. The total length of an average-sized specimen is no more than 5½ inches, with the tail accounting for about 2⅞ inches of this measurement. The scales are keeled, moderate in size, and pointed—the reason for the name "spiny." The head is rugose—that is, full of wrinkles—and the tail is tapering. The legs are slightly bowed and stocky, and end in feet provided with strong claws.

The color of this lizard may be gray, gray-green, or brown. The back is banded by a series of narrow, black lines that resemble a succession of irregular V's. The male has two large patches of blue on the underside, a distinguishing mark often absent in the female.

Some of these lizards bring forth live young. Still others lay eggs. The eastern fence lizard is one of the egg-laying species. The oval eggs are about ½ inch long and are covered with a shell that is paper-thin. The eggs of captive specimens hatch in six or eight weeks. And the young are replicas of the parents.

Neither the young nor the old eastern fence lizard makes a particularly good pet, for both are exceedingly timid. However, in a dry and sunny cage and with an abundance of live insects and mealworms, this lizard thrives and is fairly long-lived.

More than twice the size of the eastern fence lizard is the desert spiny lizard (*S. magister*), with an overall measurement of as much

GILA MONSTER
Heloderma suspectum

EASTERN
FENCE LIZARD
Sceloporus undulatus; male

COLLARED
LIZARD
Crotaphytus collaris

FIVE-LINED SKINK
Eumeces fasciatus; sub-adult male

SIX-LINED
RACERUNNER
Cnemidophorus sexlineatus; male

as 13¾ inches. This large lizard, with many pointed scales, is a ground-dwelling species. It is often found where there are yuccas, running about on the stems or hiding beneath the spines of these white-blossomed plants.

Only one other in this group reaches the size of the desert species. It is the blue spiny lizard (*S. cyanogenys*), a reptile of the lower Rio Grande Valley. It may also measure 13¾ inches from tip of snout to tip of tail.

These are only three of the spiny lizards—creatures active during the day and consequently more readily observed than related species.

HORNED LIZARDS ("TOADS")
Phrynosoma

The range of the horned lizard is in western North America, from just above the Canadian border south into Mexico. Within this area are various species and subspecies of this flattened, somewhat circular reptile, distinguished by tiny horns on the head and by a spine-covered back. Some of these lizards have horns that are not at all prominent, and consequently are classified as "short-horned."

One short-horned species is *Phrynosoma douglassi*, the lizard in the accompanying illustration. This is one of the smaller species, seldom measuring more than 4¾ inches from its blunted snout to the end of its short tail. The horns are bony extensions of the skull with a covering, and the legs are short. The range of *douglassi* is the Pacific Northwest, where the presence of the pigmy horned toad in Crater Lake National Park was definitely established in June 1952. Here, two park naturalists collected a specimen along the rim of Wheeler Creek Canyon, at an altitude of 5,500 feet. This, only the third such lizard caught in the Park, is known scientifically as *P. d. douglassi*.

The horned lizard with the greatest distribution is one distinguished by two large central head spines, a broad body, and a small, thin tail. This is the Texas horned lizard (*P. cornutum*). The dull gray or sandy gray back is covered with granular scales from which spiny projections rise at regular intervals. There is usually a crown of spines projecting from the back of the head. A yellow line starts behind the head and extends down the back and along the tail. Other identifying marks are dark splotches on each side of the neck, and three pairs of crescent-shaped dark spots on the body; each of these spots is half-circled by yellow at the rear. The yellow undersides are also darkly spotted.

The Texas horned lizard, abundant in the state for which it is named, is found as far north as Nebraska and as far south as Chihuahua and Sonora in Mexico. To the east it has been recorded for Illinois (although not recently) and in Missouri and Arkansas. To the west, it occupies territories in New Mexico and Arizona.

This lizard, like its many relatives, is an inhabitant of hot, dry, and sandy areas where the climate is apt to be subarid. It thrives under such conditions, and is most active during the hottest part of the day. It searches for small insects, particularly ants, with the deliberation of a hoptoad—perhaps one reason it is commonly called a "toad," a misnomer if there ever was one. It moves toward its prey slowly; then, when it is within striking distance, stops, bends its head ever so slightly, and unfurls its thick and sticky tongue. The insect, glued to the tip of the tongue, is brought back into the mouth so quickly that the action is barely discernible.

Late in the afternoon the lizard stops hunting, for this is the time of day it gets ready to bed down for the night. The little creature shoves its blunt nose into the warm sand, over which heat waves still dance, then moves forward to plow a shallow furrow. Next it squirms and wriggles to deepen the furrow. By strenuous body movements and with the aid of its sharp, spiny sides, it manages to squirm its way beneath the sand. Usually it does a thorough job of burying itself, but occasionally it leaves its head exposed. En-trenched like this, it becomes such a part of its surroundings that it is difficult to locate. In this way, it often escapes predators—the snakes of its region. Some horned lizards, of course, fall prey to snakes. Not all snakes survive the swallowing of such prey, for the horns break the snake's body wall and cause death.

The horned lizard also buries itself for another reason. When the first chill of autumn comes, the intervals these lizards spend buried

Short-horned Lizard,
Phrynosoma douglassi

or half-buried become longer and longer. Then at the start of the desert winter, a horned lizard buries itself deeply and passes the season in a state of suspended animation.

A horned lizard makes a good pet. In Arizona so many were captured that this reptile, like the Gila monster, is now protected there by law, and is not so easily come by as in former days. A captive needs a good-sized cage with a deeply sanded floor, and one that is kept at a temperature of at least 70° F. The cage should be set where it gets plenty of sun for the better part of the day. The cage-dweller should be fed mealworms, ants, flies, and other small insects. And for drinking water a leaf of lettuce or some similar green dipped in water is sufficient. The lizard will lap the drops off the leaf.

Some horned lizards lay eggs. The females of this group dig holes in a sandy slope with the forefeet, pushing away the loosened sand with the hind feet. The digging and pushing continue until the cavity is six inches deep. Then the female deposits twelve to thirty eggs, tough-shelled and measuring about ½ inch in length. The eggs are covered with sand, and left to be incubated by the sun.

Depending upon the species, the eggs take from a few days to several weeks to hatch.

A short-horned species such as *P. douglassi* brings forth live young in litters of five to twenty-five. A litter is delivered in a transparent protective sheathing. A young lizard, measuring about 1 ¼ inches at birth, breaks this sheathing almost at once. It emerges as a smooth-skinned creature, whose horns are no more than rudimentary. It is active immediately and, like the young of all other reptiles and amphibians, fends for itself. By the time it is fully grown it measures 2 ½ to 3 ¾ inches in overall length.

The Texas horned lizard (*P. cornutum*) is an egg-laying species. At the time of hatching one of these lizards measures about 1 ¼ inches. And when one is fully grown it may measure 2 ½ to 4 inches from tip to snout to tip of tail.

The horned lizards of North America have no close relatives anywhere in the world. However, in Australia a small lizard called the moloch or "thorny devil" (*Moloch horridus*) bears a really striking resemblance to our horned lizards. Clifford H. Pope comments on this similarity:

Here is a fine example of parallel evolution, two unrelated animals that developed a striking likeness presumably because they live under similar conditions.

NIGHT LIZARDS
Xantusia

In the high desert country of California, below Twentynine Palms, are more than half a million acres known as Joshua Tree National Monument. Here, magnificent stands of the Joshua-tree, the cholla cactus, and other unusual desert plants grow among great outcroppings of rock. Here, too, you will find the desert night lizard (*Xantusia vigilis*), a small, somewhat rare species whose lidless eyes are set with vertical pupils. This lizard is one that undergoes chromatic changes. By day, its gray, yellow, or yellow-brown color is light; but as night falls, the color deepens until the lizard is nearly as black as the shades of night.

Once this color change is complete, the desert night lizard is ready to forage among the various plants of its habitat. The little creature may have passed the day asleep under a branch of the heavy, erratic, and angular-shaped Joshua-tree or in the leafy debris at the base of one of these great yuccas. It forages over its range, darting this way and that, in search of tiny flies, small beetles, other minute insects, and the small white eggs of spiders.

As soon as dawn lightens the desert and the Joshua-trees are again in bold relief, the desert night lizard finds safety by secreting itself in or beneath one of the yuccas. The species that dwell in rocky country insert themselves between semidetached splinters of rock and the rocks proper. So secreted the lizards are safe from most predators, though some specimens are collected by man who has learned of these retreats.

The desert night lizard and its close relatives, the Arizona, the granite, and the island night lizards, are species that bear young. Some time during the late summer a female desert night lizard bears one, two, or occasionally three minute replicas of herself. By the time one of these lizards is fully grown, it measures at most 3½ inches from one end to the other. The tapering, rounded tail may account for as much as 1⅞ inches of this overall length. It has a tendency to snap off, but soon regenerates in the manner of various other lizards. Some adult lizards of this kind have three folds of skin beneath the throat, a characteristic that apparently is governed by the whereabouts of the lizard on its range.

The desert night lizard seems to be dependent upon the tree yuccas—many of which are extremely rare. One of these is the rapidly diminishing Joshua-tree, the sanctuary of the desert night lizard. The setting aside of lands for a National Monument to preserve the stands of Joshua-trees and other desert plants also means the protection of one of North America's unusual animals.

STRIPED SKINKS
Scincidae

If you have a predilection for lizards with lines running from head to tail, then you have several to choose from among the striped skinks. You may have one with two, four, or five lines, with short lines, many lines, or no lines at all. These are only six of the many striped skinks in North America—all of moderate size and all distinguished by smooth and shiny scales that protect a hard body surface. All are also distinguished by the ability to move so quickly that they are exceedingly difficult to catch.

Among this plethora of striped skinks, the five-lined species (*Eumeces fasciatus*) has the greatest distribution. It is most abundant throughout the South, with the greatest concentrations in South Carolina, Georgia, and Florida. It ranges west into Texas and north as far as Massachusetts, with another concentration in New Jersey. The species in the North do not grow so large as those in the South. But North, South, East, or West, this skink has two color phases. Its appearance when young is so entirely different from its appearance as an adult that for many years it was believed the two stages represented two different species.

A young five-lined skink—sometimes called the blue-tailed lizard—has a body shiny as jet. Five yellow lines run from below the head to the tail; one line is centered and forks on the head, whereas the others are paired on either side. The lines end abruptly at the tail, which is blue and has the hard sheen of enamel.

When the five-lined skink is in its adult phase, it undergoes the startling color change that is responsible for two other names. These are "red-headed lizard" and "scorpion." The male becomes a uniform dull brown with no sign of stripes, whereas the female retains dull stripes for life. Apparently the adult male is compensated for his loss of stripes by having an enlarged, orange-red head. In some localities the red-headed male is considered poisonous—a belief contrary to fact.

This skink flourishes in areas such as the piney-woods country of southern New Jersey and the pine barrens of South Carolina, Georgia, and Florida. In such regions it is active throughout the day, either foraging or basking in the sun in a small, convenient clearing. But whatever a skink is doing, it is always wary—ready to scurry off if an intruder comes within ten feet. And once it starts a getaway, the five-lined skink does not stop to look back. It keeps on going until it disappears into a tree hole or beneath a brush pile or other woods litter.

The skink moves about on its territory in a slithering manner, for its legs are short and weak and cannot support the body in a position for running. As it slithers along, it darts its forked tongue out and in to help locate food. It feeds upon the grubs and beetles that infest rotten wood, as well as upon various other insects, the eggs of other lizards, small-sized birds' eggs and recently hatched wood mice. The male is well equipped to eat such prey as mice, since it has strong enough jaws to give anyone handling it a painful nip. And should you grasp one by the tail, it usually comes off in your hand as its owner escapes.

The five-lined skink is an egg-laying species. After coming out of hibernation, it mates sometime during May. About six weeks later the female deposits a clutch of six to eighteen eggs in a warm, moist place—perhaps under a slab of fallen bark. Then the female broods the eggs—unusual behavior for a lizard. She stays half-coiled around the clutch for the better part of another six weeks, only taking time off for an occasional sunbath or to hunt for food. As soon as the clutch hatches, she leaves the one-inch young to shift for themselves. By the time a southern five-lined skink is fully grown, it may reach a length of 10 inches. A northern specimen may not measure much more than 6 inches from end to end.

There are only two skinks in North America that do not belong to the same genus as the striped skinks (*Eumeces*). One is the brown-backed skink (*Lygosoma laterale*), a small, bronze-colored lizard with a yellow abdomen. Also known as the ground lizard, this skink is found in the East from lower New Jersey to Florida, then west to central Texas, and north into Illinois. You are apt to find this 4-inch lizard in moist, woodsy areas, where it darts about over the ground in search of insects, snails, and worms. In turn it is preyed upon by various small snakes, including the scarlet snake (*Cemophora coccinea*), for which it is the dietary mainstay.

The wormlike sand skink (*Neoseps reynoldsi*) is the only representative of its genus in North America, and it is restricted to central and southern Florida. This rare little skink is a great burrower—probably the reason it went undiscovered until 1910. The first specimen was donated by its finder, A. G. Reynolds, to the

United States National Museum in Washington, D. C., where it now "rests" preserved in alcohol.

WHIPTAIL LIZARDS and RACERUNNERS
Cnemidophorus

Throughout the Americas and in the West Indies there are some two hundred kinds of lizards belonging to the family known scientifically as the Teiidae. In South America the family is represented by the tegus, the largest of which may measure 3 feet from end to end. In North America the Teiidae reach no such lengths, and are represented by the whiptails and racerunners, including a small species with six narrow yellow lines (*Cnemidophorus sexlineatus*).

The six-lined racerunner, the smallest species in the United States, is the only one of these lizards in the East. It is also the one with the widest distribution, with a range that includes the eastern states from Delaware to Florida, the Mississippi Valley as far north as Lake Michigan, the central states north to Nebraska, the Gulf states, and west into eastern Texas. Throughout this range the six-lined racerunner dwells in various habitats from sea level to altitudes of two thousand feet. But wherever it is, this fast-moving, dark brown reptile likes a territory that is sunny and one that affords plenty of cover.

The head of this lizard is less pointed than that of the other, allied species. The body is long and slender, and the tail is tapering and accounts for at least one-half of the maximum length of 10 inches. The legs are strong, and the blackish tongue is forked. Six yellow stripes, narrow but distinct, extend from the head to the base of the tail. The stripes are retained for life—a characteristic that is not true of all whiptails and racerunners.

The six-lined racerunner, like all its kind, is an extremely active, ground-loving reptile. In Georgia it is known as the "streak-field," an appropriate nickname, for in escaping it is said to achieve a speed of 18 miles an hour for short distances. Such a speed makes it the fastest-moving of all North American reptiles.

The home range of this racerunner may measure as much as

three hundred feet in diameter. It hunts on this domain during the day, stopping from time to time to sun itself. It generally seeks its prey in the morning and again in the evening. During the hottest part of the day the six-lined racerunner is inactive—concealed beneath low, bushy growths or hidden in a burrow of its own making, or in one abandoned by a mouse or gopher.

As it moves over its own range, the racerunner darts its forked tongue out and in, smelling the ground over which it travels. This is a great aid in helping to locate concealed foods. It eats insects of many kinds, including beetles and their larvae, crickets, and grasshoppers. It has been reported as feeding on the contents of the small eggs of ground-nesting birds. To do so, the story goes, it cracks the shell and scoops out the contents with its flat, forked tongue.

Shortly after coming out of hibernation a six-lined racerunner seeks a mate. By June or July the female is ready to lay her thin-shelled eggs. She scoops out a hole 4 to 12 inches deep, in soil that makes for easy digging, then deposits four to six eggs. The clutch, carefully covered, is left to be incubated by the sun's heat—a process that takes five to eight weeks.

Though South America has the largest of the Teiidae and North America can boast of one of the speediest, both are literally outshone by another member of the family. This is a tiny teid, known to scientists as *Proctoporus shrevei*, that lives in caves on the island of Trinidad. The male has a row of light spots on each side of the back. These spots glow in the dark, and in writing of them in *The World of Amphibians and Reptiles*, Robert Mertens says:

Nothing of a like nature occurs in the amphibians, although a tree-frog is apparently able to produce a luminous secretion.

ALLIGATOR LIZARDS
Gerrhonotus

The alligator lizards, known too as plated lizards, are named for their shape and because they have heavily keeled scales on the slender body and tail. They are further distinguished by a fold of skin, flexible and scale-covered, on each side of the body. These folds extend from behind the ears to the base of the hind legs. The head has a pointed snout, and the tail is extremely long and brittle. Sometimes it is twice the length of the head and body taken together.

These lizards are found in Mexico, parts of the Southwest, all along the Pacific coast, inland to Montana, and in an area of British Columbia. Because the range is so extensive, their home habitats vary greatly. Some frequent wooded and forested country; others inhabit rocky terrain; and still others live in lands with thick belts of chaparral—thickets of dwarf evergreen oaks that afford cover; and then there are those found at altitudes of seven to nine thousand feet or even higher. For some of these lizards live above timberline in Mexico.

One species that inhabits a part of this range is the northern alligator lizard (*Gerrhonotus coeruleus*), a brown or olive reptile with a recorded length of 15¼ inches. This is unusual, for most of these lizards grow no longer than one foot. (The southern form (*G. multicarinatus*) sometimes exceeds 20 inches in length.) The tail of the foot-long northern species is marked with dark crossbands, some of which are dotted with white. The legs are short but by no means nonfunctional.

The northern alligator lizard moves over a home range at a much more leisurely pace than that of a skink, for instance, but still makes good time. It covers its terrain with the sinuous motion of a snake and, like that reptile, flicks out its forked tongue, then draws it in. Its prey consists of slow-moving insects, smaller lizards, and various spiders—including the black widow, where its range and the alligator lizard's overlap. In turn it is prey for larger reptiles, many birds, and some mammals.

If this lizard is frightened while hunting, it streaks away as fast as it can, discarding its tail as it does so—a voluntary action. The discarded member thrashes and wriggles on the ground with such vigor that a predator is often diverted, while the lizard escapes. A new tail grows in time; it is never as long as the original; and if it is shed a second time, it is replaced by one still shorter. If you do manage to catch a male, handle it carefully, for it can give you a nasty little nip.

The alligator lizard is a species that gives birth to live young. Two to fifteen are born in a membranous envelope. Upon breaking out of this protective sheath, the little lizards, pale replicas of the parents, appear to be smooth and glossy. And once free of their natal envelope, they fend for themselves.

The northern alligator lizard is only one of sixteen species and subspecies listed by a committee of the American Society of Ichthyologists and Herpetologists. Such common names as Shasta alligator lizard, Sierra Madre alligator lizard, and San Diego alligator lizard indicate where some of these reptiles may be found.

GLASS LIZARD ("SNAKE")
Ophisaurus ventralis

> The watchful Dragon comes the Arke to keepe,
> But lul'd with murmure gently fals to sleepe:
>
> . . . .
>
> The Lizard shuts up his sharp-sighted eyes,
> Amongst these serpents, and there sadly lyes.
>
> MICHAEL DRAYTON

This lizard is commonly called the "glass snake" or the "joint snake." Its lack of legs, extremely long tail, and wriggly sidewise movements are probably the reason it is often mistaken for a snake. But movable eyelids, an undivided lower jaw, and external ear openings differentiate it from the snakes.

The upper surface of the glass lizard is black, brown, or olive. The small ringlike scales on the back have individual dots of bright green, and there are additional dots of the same color on the head and neck. Sometimes these flecks of color are so arranged that they look like narrow stripes. This is an exception to the general rule, and is found only on occasional individuals. The underside is always a greenish white.

The reason for the name "glass snake" or "joint snake" is that the tail is so easily detached. This may be voluntary, and undoubtedly serves as a defense measure. While a predator such as the king snake (*Lampropeltis getulus*) is distracted by the writhing of the detached tail, the glass lizard often makes its escape. The lost appendage is replaced in time by another, but the new tail never equals the magnificence of the original.

The range of the glass lizard in one form or another starts some miles inland from the coast in North Carolina and extends south into Florida. It is also found in the vicinity of Lake Michigan and south into Texas and northern Mexico.

Most of the glass lizard's time is spent underground, burrowing in search of earthworms and other soil-dwelling animals. When it is above ground the glass lizard prefers open fields and meadowland. As it moves about in search of a spot in which to start a new burrow, it may come across the nest of a small ground-nesting bird. It feeds on any eggs it finds. The jaws are strong enough to crack the shells, from which it ladles out the contents with its flat, forked tongue. If you catch one of these lizards, it will attempt to bite. A captive soon gets over this tendency, and learns to take food from the captor's fingers.

One of the largest glass lizards ever caught measured more than 3 feet. This specimen was presented to the Museum of Comparative Zoology at Cambridge, Massachusetts. The usual length is a little more than 2 feet, with the tail accounting for as much as 17 inches. But whatever its size, the glass lizard is one that seems to have had no use for legs, and that therefore, ages ago, dispensed with them entirely.

WORM and FOOTLESS (or LEGLESS) LIZARDS
Rhineura and *Anniella*

The family to which the worm lizard (*Rhineura floridana*) belongs has representatives in Asia, Africa, Europe, South America northward into Mexico, the West Indies, and Florida. The species in the United States is restricted to central and northern Florida. This lizard is a legless reptile so similar in appearance to an earthworm that it might easily be mistaken for one, except that its color is a faint lavender.

R. floridana spends the better part of its life underground. It feeds on the soft-bodied larvae of insects, some earthworms, and termites.

After a rainy spell the worm lizard occasionally comes to the surface. It stays above ground only long enough to locate a particularly soft spot in the dry sand of its habitat where it can dig in, thus starting another of its long tunnels. From time to time, one of these lizards is brought to light during the plowing season, when specimens are unearthed from a depth of four or five inches. As captives these lizards are not interesting because they spend most of their time in hiding.

At the time of hatching a young worm lizard measures about 4 inches in length. And by the time one is fully grown, it measures 7 to 11 inches from one end to the other. A record length for one of these lizards is 15 ⅛ inches.

The lizards belonging to the genus *Anniella* have a bewildering array of common names. One, *A. pulchra nigra*, is known as the "blind worm," the "blind snake," and the "black legless lizard." This 7 ½-inch lizard is a burrowing form, found only in the vicinity of Pacific Grove, California.

The other, better-known subspecies of this genus, *A. p. pulchra*, has the common names "silvery footless lizard" and "worm lizard." It is a small, wormlike creature of a uniform silvery gray, measuring 7 ½ inches. The gray is relieved by three dark lines, one down the center of the back and one on each side. Though its two tiny eyes are discernible, there is no sign of any external ears.

The silvery footless lizard is found in moist, sandy environments along the coast of California (except for an area in and around Monterey) from Contra Costa County southward into Baja California. It rarely surfaces, for a very little exposure to the sun is fatal.

An account of the silvery footless (or legless) lizard in *Copeia* (1932, No. 1, p. 4) concludes: "A specimen collected August 31, 1926 . . . contained two apparently fully developed embryos 69 and 66 mm. long. They are light colored with normal longitudinal lines clearly defined. They are folded three times in the egg membrane."

There is another form of worm lizard about which the writer-naturalist Peter Matthiessen remarks, "The Arizona worm lizard is so rare that, although it almost certainly occurs in southeast Arizona, according to numerous unofficial reports . . . no specimen, to date [1959], has been collected."

From unofficial reports the Arizona worm lizard seems to be similar to the species known scientifically as *Bipes biporus* of Baja California. This lizard has a pair of short, well-developed legs set so far forward on the segmented body that they seem to sprout from either side of the head. The legs are equipped with five claws, four of which are sharp. Its colors are purplish-brown and yellowish-white—a combination so evenly distributed that each covers just one-half the circumference of the body.

GILA MONSTER
Heloderma suspectum

One of the reptiles of the mesquite and creosote-bush desert is the fat and usually sluggish Gila monster. It is the largest lizard north of the Rio Grande, the only poisonous one in the United States, and the only venomous reptile protected by law. It is closely related to the Mexican beaded lizard, the only other poisonous lizard in the world.

The Gila monster is covered with innumerable beadlike scales in a combination of black and some other color—gray, gray-white, yellow-white, orange, or salmon pink. This colored beading is the reason for its generic name *Heloderma*, meaning "nail-studded skin." Its specific name, *suspectum*, was selected because for many years this lizard was merely thought to be poisonous, whereas the Mexican beaded lizard (*H. horridum*) was known to be.

The lizard with the nail-studded skin may measure as much as 2 feet, including its fat, blunted tail. The tail is important, for it serves as a food reservoir in which fats are stored to be used as nourishment during times when little or no prey is available, or when the animal is inactive. When small mammals, eggs of such ground-nesting birds as Gambel's quail, and other lizards are plentiful, the tail is thick and swollen. When food is scarce, the tail is thin and attenuated. The short, chubby legs, also beaded, end in feet with five claws. And the eyes are set in the sides of the somewhat flattened head that usually has a crown of one of the lighter colors.

During the day the Gila monster secretes itself under rocks or burrows in the sand to avoid the heat. During the night it hunts some of the other nocturnal members of its desert community. It kills small mammal prey such as mice and rabbits by biting them, then injecting venom into the victim. The biting jaws grind from side to side, with the poison coming through the grooved teeth at the back. The venom, with an odor similar to that of calamus, is contained in two sacs embedded in the lower jaw. It is as toxic as the venom of the coral snake, and works in a similar way. For it is a neural toxin, one that attacks the nervous system, whereas the toxin of some rattlesnakes, for instance, is hemal, affecting the blood cells (see page 23).

The Gila monster is not given to attack, for like many other animals it minds its own business if left alone. If provoked, however, it turns on an enemy with surprising agility, hissing as it does so, and then attacks. Though fatalities resulting from the bite of the Gila monster are few, six have been recorded. And even some of these are open to doubt. Anyone bitten by this lizard generally experiences a painful and extensive swelling in the vicinity of the bite.

Dr. Herbert L. Stahnke, of Arizona State College at Tempe, was once bitten by a Gila monster during his long study of this reptile. He combated the effects of the bite and injected poison with applications of ice. In addition to such a measure, anyone bitten by a Gila monster should use the treatment prescribed for the bites of poisonous snakes.

Dr. Stahnke recovered from the Gila's bite, and went on with the study of the lizard, started in 1939. The Doctor and his advanced herpetology students made semiannual field trips in search of Gilas. They collected specimens in the Salt River valley of Maricopa County each spring and fall. Two or three lizards were usually captured on a trip. By 1947, however, Dr. Stahnke and his students noted that Gila monsters were hard to come by, and in some formerly productive areas there were none.

Upon investigation the Doctor discovered there was such a good market for this country's only poisonous lizard that it was being sold at roadside zoos and reptile gardens. The dealers in live Gilas were paying local trappers twenty-five to fifty cents an inch; in turn the lizards were being sold to out-of-state dealers at one to two dollars an inch. And the traffic was such that the animal would soon be trapped out on its restricted range in the Lower Sonoran Life Zone. Moreover, there was little chance of raising Gilas in captivity, for this lizard does not reproduce readily under controlled conditions.

Shortly after Dr. Stahnke revealed the Gila's precarious position, it was protected by law in Arizona. Now you must get permission in writing from the state Game and Fish Commission to carry on any sort of work with the Gila monster or the little horned lizard— another reptile that has become rare because it was caught and sold.

Throughout its small range the female Gila monster lays her eggs some time during late July or the first weeks of August. With her front feet she scoops out a basinlike depression of three to five inches. She usually deposits four to seven eggs, though a clutch may consist of as few as three or as many as thirteen. She covers the large, soft-shelled eggs with sand, then leaves them to be hatched by the elements—a combination of moisture and heat. The eggs hatch a month or so later and the young then wriggle and squirm to the surface. A recently hatched Gila monster is a miniature of the parents, and measures 6 inches or so from tip of snout to tip of tail. The coloring is much more vivid than that of the adults.

The Gila monster takes kindly to captivity, taming so quickly that it soon allows its head to be scratched. Such intimacy, however, should be left to the experienced handler of reptiles. One quirk of the captive Gila is its liking to soak for hours at a time in any available water. And in captivity it eats liquid food by lapping it up with its long, forked tongue, then raising its head so that the liquid can run down its throat.

In exceedingly hot weather or during the winter months, captive and wild Gilas become sluggish and inactive. To escape desert heat, a wild Gila holes up in burrows or crevices. During such a quiescent interval it is sustained by the concentrated fats in its tail. It lives by the same means during its short hibernation within an area watered by the Gila River—the river from which the only poisonous lizard in the United States gets its common name.

THE LAST OF THE LIZARDS

The species written about so far represent some of the lizards of North America. But no account should omit mention of the fringe-toed lizard (*Uma notata*), one of the iguanids of the United States. This lizard is a fast-moving species restricted to arid areas where the sands are ever-shifting and built into dunes as the winds landscape desert country. In one of three forms the fringe-toed lizard thrives in the Mojave and Colorado deserts.

An adult fringe-toed lizard occasionally attains an overall length of 8½ inches. But whether short or long, it is light in color as befits a creature living under desert conditions. It has a small, flattened head and a tail that is also flattened. The hind legs are longer than the forelegs and have spiny fringes that are also longer than those on the forelegs. So equipped it can indulge in a form of locomotion known as "sand swimming."

One of these lizards on-the-run races over the top of a dune, then dives into the softer sand on the far side. It moves along beneath the surface for a short distance, using its strong hind legs in a style similar to the one employed by a man swimming under water. Such dives are not always successful. For a lizard often takes a slope with an angle of thirty-five degrees at such a speed that it shoots into the air and goes over the top. The speed of the fringe-toed lizard in flight was reported in *Natural History* (November 1952), by Kenneth S. Norris. Driving a jeep across a sandy waste, he clocked one at 15 miles an hour.

The fringe-toed lizard is by nature a vegetarian. It feeds on the leaves of a forget-me-not that flourishes in sand-dune country. It also eats the young leaves of the desert willow, and even climbs high into this tree to reach them. As a predator it hunts ants, bees, caterpillars, and flies. It takes flies on the wing, leaping into the air to capture them. This penchant for acrobatic hunting makes the fringe-toed lizard one of North America's most spectacular species.

TURTLES AND
TORTOISES

"All thoughts of a turtle are turtles . . ."
RALPH WALDO EMERSON
The Natural History of the Intellect

Turtles belong to the order Testudines, a small group of animals distinguished by shields that protect the soft body parts. Throughout the world there are fewer than 225 such animals. And in North America and the warm seas and oceans around it there are between fifty and sixty species.

The Testudines are known variously as turtles, tortoises, and terrapins. There is no precise rule concerning the use of these popular names. *Turtle* may be applied to any member of this animal group. As a rule, *tortoise* is used for the terrestrial forms, such as the box turtle or tortoise and the huge species found on the Galápagos Islands. And *terrapin* generally designates the edible species living in fresh or brackish water—especially those known as diamondback terrapins.

The turtles, the tortoises, and the terrapins have undergone little change during millions of years. And they are outstanding in their class because they are the only reptiles with shells or shields.

A dorsal shield, called the carapace, is the topside covering, and a ventral shield, known as the plastron, protects the underside. Most of the world's turtles have rigid carapaces. But those of a single large genus are distinguished by "shells" that are soft and flexible, as compared to the horny shields of other turtles. These softshell species occur in North America and the Old World.

Today's turtles are not nearly so large as their ancestors. The rocks of the Tertiary era have disclosed that once there were tortoises whose shells had a diameter of 10 feet. Probably these giant land turtles died before the start of the Tertiary—perhaps they died long before the reptiles lost their dominion of the earth to the mammals.

The crocodile and the alligator give us an idea of what certain animals looked like in the long ago and far away. This is also true of the various turtles, whose activity is affected by prevailing temperatures because they are cold-blooded like the rest of their class and like the amphibians from which they descended.

MARINE TURTLES
Cheloniidae and Dermochelidae

The marine turtles are the heaviest of all living reptiles. They are also the largest of all the turtles. These ocean-going animals are distinguished by legs ending in flippers similar to those of the seal, and they are even more aquatic than this sea mammal. A fur seal spends a part of each year ashore, during the breeding and birthing season. But it is only the female marine turtle that comes ashore when it is time to deposit her eggs in coastal sands, well beyond tideline.

On occasion a marine turtle forsakes the safety of the warm reaches of the Atlantic or the Pacific, and in the throes of what might be considered a wayward impulse swims north in the mild waters of the Gulf Stream or the Japan Current. In the Atlantic this trek often takes one to coastal waters off the south shore of Long Island, New York, or those off Connecticut and Massachusetts. A few individuals have continued swimming north until they reached the waters around Nova Scotia. In the Pacific, marine species have been noted as far north as Nootka Sound, a natural harbor on the west coast of Vancouver Island, British Columbia.

Seemingly the species most prone to wandering is the leatherback (Dermochelys coriacea), also known as the trunk turtle or the harp turtle. This dark brown or black turtle can be differentiated from other marine species by the seven lengthwise ridges on the carapace. The upper shell differs in another way, too, for it is similar to soft leather and somewhat oily.

Leatherback Turtle,
Dermochelys coriacea

The carapace of the leatherback is not the only characteristic that sets it apart from other turtles. This species is the largest of all living turtles—sometimes having a shell that measures 8 feet in length. A not unusual weight for a leatherback is 1,500 pounds, and at least one is known to have weighed 2,000 pounds. A turtle of this size can easily pull an 18-foot sailboat two miles before tiring, and has done so when harpooned.

The leatherback fares well enough during a summer sojourn in northern Atlantic waters. But as the season wanes and hurricanes from the South lash their way up the Atlantic coast, the animal is victimized by the temperature and the elements. The seasonal change causes it to become more and more sluggish until the hour arrives when it is no longer able to move. Now the huge inert form is tossed about by winds of hurricane force, in water from which the warmth of summer is gone. Finally it is cast ashore by great curling waves, white-crested and whipped into action by one of the storms born above the very waters of its normal range.

In addition to the leatherback, other marine species of the Atlantic classed as North American turtles are the green (*Chelonia mydas*), the hawksbill (*Eretmochelys imbricata*), and the loggerhead (*Caretta caretta*).

The green turtle has a head protected by dull brown or olive plates edged with white. The carapace is pale olive with tracings of yellow—a color that is repeated in the plastron. The name of this turtle does not come from the color of the carapace but from the fat, which has a greenish cast.

Of all the marine species the green turtle has the most savory flesh. Consequently it is hunted throughout an extensive range that takes in the warmer latitudes of the Atlantic, the Gulf of Mexico, and the South Pacific, including the waters around Australia, where the inhabitants of Arnhem Land hunt it from dugouts.

Today an attempt is being made to extend the range of the green turtle in the Caribbean area. The Caribbean Conservation Commission is working closely with the government of Costa Rica in an effort to restore this herbivorous turtle to some of its former pasturage and beach nesting areas. For historically this marine species used a number of nesting areas. Now the green turtle comes ashore in significant numbers for egg-laying only at Tortuguero on the coast of Costa Rica.

At the suggestion of Dr. Archie Carr, a University of Florida graduate research professor, a five-mile stretch of the Tortuguero beach was reserved for the exclusive use of the green turtle. Now turtles hatched at Tortuguero are caught and then carried to other beaches throughout the Caribbean area. It is the hope of the Commission and of the government of Costa Rica that upon maturing the released turtles will return to the point of release rather than go back to the point of hatching.

The hawksbill, smallest of the marine turtles, is also hunted by man. Its carapace is the source of tortoise shell. The carapace has shields that are imbricate; that is, they overlap one another like the slates or shingles of a roof. The shields are dark brown or nearly black and marked with yellow in a formless pattern known as marbling. The carapace of a good-sized hawksbill may yield as much as eight pounds of "shell." Most shell is processed in the Orient, with some of the finest exported from the Celebes. Now tortoise shell is so well simulated that only an expert can tell the true from the synthetic.

The loggerhead, another frequenter of warm Atlantic waters,

is dull brown on top and dull yellow underneath. Though of less commercial value as a food than the green turtle, it is hunted for its meat. This appears on the market cut like a steak and looks very much like beef.

The turtles of the Atlantic and those of the Pacific, including another leatherback species (*D. schlegeli*), have larger clutches of eggs than the land species, and are likely to lay them more than once a year. A female may come ashore two, three, or even four times each year to deposit her eggs. The clutch of a marine turtle contains 90 to 150 eggs—often many more if the female is old. And she may be rather old, for many turtles live longer than man's traditional life span.

On a night bright with moonlight the female comes ashore to deposit her eggs. She swims up from a depth of 150 feet, strikes out for the coastline, then surfaces as near a landfall as possible. She splashes through the shallows, her dark shell dripping and glistening in the moonlight, then lumbers up the beach until she is 50 to 70 feet from the water's edge.

At a point that must meet her specifications for a nest, she starts to dig. She uses her hind flippers more than those in front, making the dry surface sand fly as she starts what will be a well-defined hole. As she excavates her eyes fill with tears—Nature's way of keeping them free of the flying sand. Sometimes a leatherback digs a cavity that equals the reach of its flippers. Such a cavity is often deep enough to be waist-high on the average man.

When the female exhausts her reach, she is ready to deposit her eggs—which differ from hen's eggs in that they cannot be hard-boiled because the whites do not coagulate. As soon as the last egg is expelled, she covers the lot with the greatest of care. Next she smooths over the nest hole, then hauls herself back and forth over the area around the nest like a road-scraper. She continues this grading and smoothing until no sign of the nest is evident. Once the camouflage is complete, she abandons the nest and returns to the sea.

Six or eight weeks later the eggs hatch, and seemingly the sand spews forth young leatherbacks. A young turtle of this kind is more precocious than the young of other marine species. For some young marine turtles do not put out to sea at once, but tarry in shallow inlets that provide a little protection from such predators as larger fishes and sea birds. Here they remain until they are old enough and strong enough to head for deep water. But upon hatching the young leatherback heads directly for the open sea—swimming strongly and rapidly, and even diving during its first days in the water.

As soon as a young leatherback is in the sea, it starts a lifetime feeding on jellyfishes and mollusks. It eats these in such quantities that by the time it is an adult, it has increased its weight fifteen thousand times, according to an article in *Texas Game and Fish*, July 1952. If man were to increase his weight proportionately, by the time he was an adult he would tip the scales at fifty tons.

The leatherback does not swim so fast as the loggerhead or the green turtle. These two can cut through the water at a rate of 22 miles an hour. This makes the loggerhead and the green turtle two of the swiftest among the Tetrapoda—vertebrates characterized by "two sets of paired appendages for locomotion."

NONMARINE TURTLES

The nonmarine turtles are fairly numerous on all continents with the exception of Europe, where there are only a few. Territory in which there are no turtles at all includes the tip of South America and the colder regions of the northern continents. Parts of the world in which you will find quantities of turtles are southeastern Asia, central and southern Africa, and the eastern United States.

Except for a rare fresh-water turtle living in the Fly River in New Guinea, none of the turtles found on land or in fresh and brackish waters matches the size of seagoing relatives; nor does it have flippers. Its short, stumpy legs end in feet with five toes. The variation in size among nonmarine turtles is great; it ranges from the 4-inch mud turtle to that behemoth, the alligator snapping turtle, whose length is at least 24 inches and whose weight is 100 to 150 pounds.

SNAPPING TURTLES
Common: *Chelydra serpentina*
Alligator: *Macrochelys temmincki*

The common snapping turtle is well known to trotline and bank-line fishermen as a nuisance; to gourmets as the ingredient of a savory stew or soup; to those who handle it as a vicious animal that must be kept well beyond biting distance; and to the herpetologist Raymond L. Ditmars as "sinister."

The turtle so categorized has a large, ugly head, a long tail similar

Snapping Turtle, *Chelydra serpentina*

in shape to that of an alligator, and strong clawed feet, partially webbed to facilitate swimming. The upper shell is rough and frequently covered with green algae—which does nothing to enhance the snapper's appearance because it makes the animal look moldy. The lower shell is small and dirty yellow, and is in the form of a rough cross. And the exposed fleshy parts have a decidedly greenish tint.

The snapper is a thoroughly aquatic turtle. It is found in muddy waters from the central part of southern Canada east to Nova Scotia; in the entire eastern half of the United States from Maine to Florida; in the central states south through a part of Texas; and in northern Mexico along the Gulf.

In and around Williamsburg, Virginia, men called "snapper

trappers" devote most of the summer to catching these turtles. They sell the catches to a seafood packing plant on the Chickahominy River. For the most part these trappers are commercial fishermen who make extra money by "turtlin' " from April to September—the season when the turtles are active. Many of the snappers are caught in private farm fish ponds. Such ponds are frequently stocked with sport fish by individual farmers who lease the fishing rights—a source of immediate cash income. Too many snappers in a farm fish pond, or in any other body of water for that matter, can mean too few fish. For snappers eat some game fish and devour some fish eggs. These turtles also prey on ducklings and goslings early in the season.

The *Maryland State Conservationist* has called the snapping turtle "a friend and foe to Maryland wildlife." This comment applies to the snapper throughout its entire range. The turtle is a natural control that keeps rough or forage fishes, including the carp, within bounds. Thus it helps to maintain a balance between predator and prey, though it may spoil the good it does by including some of the more desirable fishes in its diet.

Like all other present-day reptiles, the snapping turtle has survived and perpetuated itself for centuries. It hatches from a round, white egg so elastic that it bounces. Early in summer the female leaves the water and wanders about on land until she locates a spot where the soil is soft. This is often some distance from the water. She shovels out a shallow cavity and squirms around on the bottom of it until she manages to get herself well covered with dirt. She remains half buried while depositing her nearly spherical eggs, generally numbering about two dozen, though as many as seventy-seven have been reported in a clutch. As soon as the last egg is expelled, she clambers out of the hole in an anglewise fashion. There is a method in her coming out slantwise, because the earth then falls back over the eggs.

The eggs ordinarily hatch in ninety days. When a young snapper breaks out of its shell, it is a uniform black—a color replaced at maturity by dark brown in the upper shell, which is notched along the rear edge. The lower shell is yellow and leaves much of the flesh exposed.

This turtle is a voracious feeder all its life—approximately twenty-five years—and can catch practically anything that swims. The snapper eats a wide variety of fishes, frogs of all kinds, the young of both wild and domesticated waterfowl, and young aquatic mammals including the muskrat.

Most prey is seized under water. A foraging snapper comes up beneath swimming prey, shoots out its long neck like a striking snake, and nabs whatever it is after between powerful jaws. Such prey as frogs and fishes are torn apart and swallowed piecemeal as soon as possible. A young duck, goose, or muskrat is yanked beneath the surface, dragged to the bottom, and clawed apart before it is eaten.

The snapper pursues its prey from early spring until temperatures become so low that the animal is forced to hibernate. It burrows deep in the mud of the same body of water in which it was active during spring, summer, and early fall. The length of this dormant period depends upon the whereabouts of the snapper on its range; the snappers in the North remain inactive longer than those in the South.

Though this turtle does not ordinarily estivate, a hot, rainless season may force it to do so—if much evaporation occurs. The water in an artificial lake in Centre County, Pennsylvania, was reduced by the fall of 1951 to little more than a puddle because of a nearly rainless summer and undue evaporation.

The snapping turtles (*C. s. serpentina*) of this lake quit their puddle for the shoreline. Here they dug down into the mud that rimmed the lake, and were not seen again until the water level was nearly normal. A member of the Pennsylvania Fish Commission believes that the action of these Centre County snappers indicated actual estivation.

A hibernating or estivating snapping turtle is a harmless snapping turtle. An active snapping turtle is a "hateful handful," in the words of the Virginians who trap them for a livelihood. The safest way to handle a snapper is to hold it by the long tail and at arm's length.

This precaution is necessary because the snapper has an extremely mobile neck and head, which it swivels from side to side or bends backward. It can maneuver its biting end with such speed that anyone off guard may have a chunk of flesh gouged out or a finger sheared off.

A close relative of the common snapping turtle is the largest of our fresh-water turtles. This is the species known as the alligator snapping turtle. It is found in the southern part of the Mississippi drainage, then east to Florida and west into a part of eastern Texas, where fossils from the Pleistocene have been unearthed along the Brazos River.

The alligator snapping turtle spends most of its time half concealed in the mud on the bottoms of streams, lakes, rivers, and ponds. It waits here with its huge mouth open to its greatest width, constantly wiggling a filament of flesh. This is attached to the pinkish tongue. It acts as a lure, attracting hungry fish within reach of the predator's powerful jaws.

The upper shell of this turtle is ridged by three keels and often measures 25 inches from front to back; the width may be as much as 20 inches. The average weight is 100 pounds. But some specimens have been weighed in at 150 pounds, and there are unverified reports of 200-pound catches.

The alligator snapping turtle is a creature with such a secretive way of life that few particulars of its history are available. The only known life spans are those of zoo specimens. Under the controlled conditions prevailing in zoological parks, alligator snapping turtles are on record as having lived forty and fifty years.

MUSK AND MUD TURTLES
Kinosternidae

"... on the chin there are a few, paired, short fleshy appendages or barbels; other turtles of the United States . . . lack such appendages."
CLIFFORD H. POPE, *The Reptile World*

Some North American animals are so restricted in range that they are classified as regional. Such an animal is the flattened musk turtle (*Sternotherus depressus*)—a unique species in that the upper shell is not arched like those of its close relatives. To find this atypical species you will have to go to the area of the Black Warrior River in northwest Alabama.

Of much wider distribution is the common musk turtle (*S. odoratus*), a species known also as "stinkpot" and "stinkin' Jenny." The scientific and common names as well as the nicknames are appropriate, for this turtle has glands on either side of the body from which it discharges what one natural-history writer calls "a pall of noxious odors." This pall comes from a yellowish fluid that has an odor similar to that of skunk musk but one which is not so overpowering. It is expelled in times of danger, and possibly it may be used as a means of attracting a mate.

The common musk turtle is found in slow-moving waters in southern Canada and throughout the eastern third of the United States as far south as Florida. Its range also extends west to Missouri, Oklahoma, and southern Texas. It is so thoroughly aquatic that it does not even leave the water to bask in the sun. As soon as the spring suns warm the shallow waters on the musk turtle's range, all the "stinkpots" and "stinkin' Jennies" of an area gather to take a wet sunbath, floating on or just beneath the surface. And this is the time when they are most easily caught.

This turtle is a bottom feeder, and crawls about on stream or river bed on webbed feet while it forages. It is primarily carnivorous, eating small fishes and fish eggs, tadpoles, snails, and aquatic insects, and some bits of vegetation. It also feeds on dead fishes and waterfowl, and this predilection makes the musk turtle a sort of sanitary engineer within its own community. But the good it does as an individual cleanup squad is offset by its manner of feeding. Its endless crawling about on stream or river bottom probably inhibits plant growth, and makes the water turbid.

In the late spring the female leaves the roiled waters of her environment to lay her elliptical white eggs, whose shells are hard and brittle. A single mating may suffice to produce fertile eggs for three or four years—a fact proved in a study during which the females were separated from the males after mating was consummated. In natural surroundings the female deposits three to seven eggs in one of a variety of "nests." Sometimes she expels them on top of the mud without even bothering to cover them. At other times she secretes them among decaying reeds or in a rotting stump. As soon as the full clutch is laid, she returns immediately to the water, after having spent perhaps as much as three-quarters of an hour ashore. The humidity, the heat of the sun, and that of the rotting wood or decaying reeds help to incubate the eggs. Depending upon the weather the period of incubation is sixty to ninety days, give or take a little.

At hatching a young musk turtle has an upper shell that measures ½ inch in length. By the time it is a year old this species is mature; and when it is fully grown the narrow, ovoid upper shell measures 3 or 4 inches from one end to the other. Highly arched, the upper shell is dull brown, and as the animal grows older it usually becomes coated with algae and slime. The dark brown or yellow undershell is small—a physical characteristic which sets this species apart from many other aquatic turtles. The head is large, and marked with two yellow stripes on each side. These start near the beaked snout and extend backward to the neck, to separate in front of the eyes; one stripe curves upward above the eye and the other circles below it. These lines are one of the easiest ways by which to identify the common musk turtle—a turtle that has been described as a snapper in miniature.

In the egg state and as a hatchling the common musk turtle has some enemies. Raccoons and skunks, and possibly such birds as crows and herons, dig out the eggs and eat them. And crows and muskrats prey on recently hatched young.

Even though the common musk turtle tries to bite and expel its musk, it makes a fine pet. The aquarium requirements are minimal; it can live in deep water without any rock or rocks to crawl out upon, for every so often it swims to the surface for a breath of air. It frequently seeks the protection of any bottom cover provided, but comes out to feed readily on nearly anything offered. Easily adaptable to aquarium life, it lives a long time in captivity. Dr. Doris Cochran, Curator of Reptiles and Amphibians at the U. S. National Museum, reports that one captive musk turtle lived twenty-three years.

Another member of the family Kinosternidae is the common mud turtle (*Kinosternon subrubrum*)—a species that sometimes frequents the same environment as the common musk turtle. You can identify *K. subrubrum* because the brown or olive upper shell is broader and flatter than that of its close relative. The lower shell is light brown or yellow and is divided into two hinged lobes of equal size.

These lobes can be closed against the lower edge of the upper shell. Thus the mud turtle protects itself by pulling in head, legs, and tail, and enclosing these fleshy parts within the confines of its own shell.

If you are looking for a specimen of this thoroughly aquatic turtle, you are likely to find it in slow-moving or still waters of the coastal plain from Connecticut to Florida, and inland as far as Indiana and eastern Illinois. Regional forms, or races, are found in northwest Alabama, as well as in the Gulf states, in central Florida, in some central states, and in various parts of the Southwest.

The life history and behavior of the common mud turtle are not nearly so well known as those of some other turtles. Therefore if you are looking for a natural-history project, the study of this reptile might be a worthwhile endeavor, not only for yourself, but because your observations might make a contribution to the field of herpetology.

Of course some information about the common mud turtle is a matter of record. Though slightly larger than the common musk turtle and quite capable of expelling its own "pall of noxious odors," this species is much less aggressive. It is strictly aquatic and feeds in its natural environment by crawling around on the bottom of a lake or stream, looking for all forms of small aquatic life. If you catch a fully grown specimen, you will be able to record these average measurements and identifying marks:

Carapace (end to end)	3½ to 4 inches
Carapace (side to side)	2½ inches
Plastron (end to end)	3 inches
Lobes, lower shell	1½ inches each
Identifying marks (head) . . .	yellow-green spots

Like the common musk turtle, the common mud turtle makes an excellent aquarium pet. It is the more active of the two, for it never seems to tire of swimming, though now and then it interrupts its solo aquacade to surface in order to breathe. One captive mud turtle had a record life span of nearly forty years.

The musk and the mud turtles are little liked by fishermen, for they take a baited hook faster than you can write *Kinosternidae*. The fight a hooked turtle puts up gives the impression that a "big one" has been caught. As soon as a fisherman discovers what he has on the end of his line, elation gives way to anger. In getting either of these turtles off the hook, the fisherman is sure to be further enraged when he inhales the rank odor of the musk. Fortunately this musk does not adhere like that of the skunk. It can be washed off the hands, though it may take more than one scrubbing to do so.

The only times of year you can fish without possible interference from these turtles are during late fall, winter, and early spring. Then they are hibernating. The musk turtle buries itself in bottom mud to do so, but the mud turtle is said to quit the water to pass the winter ashore in a burrow of its own digging.

BLANDING'S TURTLE
Emys blandingi

. . . one of the least aggressive of turtles . . .
DORIS M. COCHRAN,
U. S. National Museum

This fresh-water turtle is named for William Blanding, a herpetologist active in Philadelphia around 1812. A strictly northern

Mud Turtle,
Kinosternon subrubrum

species of uneven distribution, it is most numerous in the area around the Great Lakes, with some found in the vicinity of the Welland Canal and along the St. Lawrence River in Canada. To the east it has an extremely spotty distribution from New England to northern New Jersey, and to the west the range includes a small area in eastern Nebraska. Throughout its range this uncommon turtle frequents shallow, plant-filled waters, marshes and swamps, and other low, wet-land areas.

Blanding's turtle is sometimes called the "semi-box turtle" because the plastron is hinged. The forward half closes tightly, but the rear half shuts only part way, and thus this turtle does not have the maximum security of the box turtle (*Terrapene carolina*). When scared a Blanding's turtle stays within its shell for hours at a time.

The center of the lower shell is yellow, edged with irregular splotches of black. The black or dark olive upper shell is arched, and each of its shields is patterned with yellow dots. The black head is also dotted with same color, whereas the bright yellow of the chin and throat is unmarked. The feet are webbed and the neck is long, ending in a cylindrical head.

Blanding's turtle feeds with equal ease either under water or out on land. It prowls through marshy areas, searching for all kinds of berries, the tender shoots of plants, and larval forms of insects. In the water it pursues minnows, tadpoles, and other immature water animals. It catches its prey by darting out its long neck, then seizing its victim between its jaws, the upper one of which is sharply pointed.

Though Blanding's turtle may mate in the fall, it may more often do so during May. The female deposits her elliptical, white eggs, either in the afternoon or early evening. An egg-laying female was observed in the vicinity of the old Welland Canal. J. Roland Brown describes the act in "A Blanding's Turtle Lays Its Eggs," (*Canadian Field-Naturalist*, 1927):

It planted its fore feet in the sand and with its hind feet, using them alternately, gradually hollowed out a hole. The hole at first was only the width of its foot, about an inch wide. It would put its left foot in, scrape around the inside of the hole, then lift out the sand turning its

TEXAS TORTOISE
Gopherus berlandieri; young

**MIDLAND
PAINTED TURTLE**
Chrysemys picta marginata; male

EASTERN BOX TURTLE
Terrapene carolina carolina

COMMON MUSK TURTLE
(Stinkpot)
Sternotherus odoratus

MAP TURTLE
Graptemys geographica; female

**RED-EARED
TURTLE**
Pseudemys scripta elegans

foot sideways in the form of a scoop. Now it would put its right foot in and repeat the action. . . . The hole gradually became bigger until it measured five inches in depth, two inches wide at the top, and four inches wide at the bottom.

While digging the last part of its hole it put so much energy into the work that its jaws clicked under the strain.

At eight-twenty P.M. it stopped digging and rested with its right foot in the hole.

Since the female started work on her nest at seven-thirty, it had taken her fifty minutes to prepare the spot for her eggs. She rested briefly upon completing the nest, then discharged eleven eggs during an interval that lasted twenty-eight and three-quarters minutes. After the last egg was expelled she rested again before covering the clutch with sand. The turtle, Mr. Brown goes on to say, "required one hour and thirty-five minutes to satisfy itself that the eggs were safely stowed away. It very slowly moved away from the nest, packing the sand as it moved. At ten twenty-three P.M. it crawled away . . ."

The only obvious difference between a full-grown male Blanding's turtle and a female of the same species is in the tail. A male's tail is longer, slightly more than a third of the length of the carapace; that of the female is usually one-fourth the length of the carapace. The size of one of these turtles when fully grown is approximately that of one from North Judson, Indiana, described by Raymond L. Ditmars:

Length of carapace	7 ⅞ inches
Width of carapace	5 inches
Length of plastron	7 ½ inches
Length of front lobe	3 ¼ inches
Width at hinge	4 inches
Height of combined shell	2 ⅞ inches

When cold fronts from the north push down into the territory of Blanding's turtle, it seeks safety by hibernating in the bottom mud of some water area or under piles of leaves. Here it stays in a stupor until spring works its way up from the south, and rouses the turtle from its deathlike winter sleep.

BOX TURTLE
Terrapene carolina

The tortoise, or turtle, is appropriately called "an animal in a box." It is an animal with a backbone; and a most singular specimen of the back-boned, or vertebrate animal it is. . . . Here is an animal that has a bony skeleton both inside and outside. The inside bones of the turtle grow through the flesh and spread over the body above and below, making a box with holes for the head and the legs to pass out and in.

So states a McGuffey Natural History Reader published in 1888. A more fitting description of the eastern and western box turtles and their allies would be hard to find. For each of these land-dwelling turtles, including an odd three-toed race (*T. c. triunguis*), is enclosed in a box which serves it as a fortress.

The domed upper shell, the carapace, of the box turtle is a rigid shield decorated with splotches of yellow. The lower shell, the plastron, is yellow and hinged or jointed across the midsection. This flexible piece makes it possible for one of these turtles to open and close the two sections of the lower shell at will.

If the box turtle is threatened it shuts itself up. First it pulls in its head, its stumpy legs, and its short, pointed tail; then it secures these members by closing both halves of the plastron. These halves fit into the upper shell with such precision that you cannot insert even the edge of a paper-thin instrument between them. Not all box turtles have such snug-fitting lower shells; the subspecies in Florida, for example, is not so well equipped as *T. carolina*.

There are times when the box turtle cannot contain itself within its shell, for it is something of a glutton. When wild blackberries, blackcaps, or strawberries are fruiting, the box turtle is likely to overindulge its appetite for these seasonal delicacies. After such gorging, the turtle is often temporarily too big for its own box, and is unable to close both front and rear halves simultaneously. If you find a turtle whose rear legs and tail are out but whose head and forelegs are in, you can be reasonably sure that it is one which has been the victim of its own appetite.

The box turtle also feeds on variety of leafy green vegetables, including wild and cultivated lettuce, and on wild mushrooms, snails, earthworms, grasshoppers, and other insects and their larvae. It has been charged with eating the eggs and young of ground-nesting birds. This charge has not been fully substantiated; it is possible that the box turtle is only finishing what some predator has left untouched.

On its search for these foods the box turtle wanders over a large home range. Its preferred environment is moist, rather open woods or swampy land with open, fieldlike spots. In the East the box turtle's range extends from Maine to the tip of Florida, and west to an area on the far side of the Mississippi River. Another form of box turtle replaces the eastern species in Illinois. You will find the western box turtle (*T. ornata*) in this state and as far west as the Rocky Mountains, and south into Arizona, New Mexico, and Texas.

If you spend a little time in the field you can learn to differentiate the male box turtle from the female. The simplest method is by a comparison of the little round eyes. Usually the male has bright red eyes, the female yellow, gray brown, or dark red. If you locate two unfrightened box turtles, you may note that one has a tail slightly longer than the other. The one with the longer tail is the male. And if you come upon one of these turtles unexpectedly, it may hiss. This is an audible expression of fright, not a signal that you are about to be attacked. For the box turtle is one of the gentlest of wild creatures, and makes a fine pet that in time learns to take bits of hamburger from your fingers.

In the late spring or early summer the male's meandering course is sure to cross the equally haphazard route of a female. This happenstance meeting is the beginning of a courtship initiated by the male. He follows the female as she ambles first this way and then that across the forest floor, through swamp or field, or in the sandy places of the Southwest.

The female plods along, seemingly oblivious of the trailing male. Suddenly, as if irritated at being ignored, the male speeds up his shambling gait. As soon as he is within biting distance, he gently nips her back legs. If she ignores these overtures and starts on, the male anchors her to the spot by raising himself sufficiently to put his forelegs on her back. As soon as the mating interval is over, the two separate and each resumes its solitary wandering.

The female spends the remainder of the summer in eating and roaming around. By the time the first cold fronts in the North hint at the coming of winter, the female has usually found a suitable spot for hibernating. This is where the soil is not too dry and one where it is loose. This combination permits easy digging—a prime requisite, for she may have to dig several feet to reach a point beyond frost line.

This line varies within the range of the box turtle. On the most northerly parts of its range in the East, it may be as much as 60 inches beneath the earth's surface. In the east central states the frost line varies from 10 to 15 inches, depending upon the severity of the winter. If a turtle digs down a foot and one half, it can overwinter in safety. And in the South the digging distance is slight, for the frost line is not more than 5 inches—usually the greatest depth to which frost penetrates in the Carolinas.

A female on the northern part of the range may hibernate for as long as six months, whereas one farther south will be dormant for a much shorter period. The ornate box turtle of the Southwest is quiescent for three months. But whether short or long, this is a period during which the turtle is in a state of suspended animation— a deathlike sleep characterized by a greatly lowered metabolic rate. And it lasts until the frost goes out of the ground and the spring suns again warm the land, or until the rains moisten the dry areas of the Southwest. April is the month in which many a box turtle rouses. It emerges into a world that is redolent with the freshness of spring and bright with the new green of unfolding leaves and sprouting vegetation.

A female recently released from hibernation soon seeks a place to deposit her eggs—fertilized from last year's mating or from one that occurred three, or even four, years previously. She seeks a sunny spot, where she hollows out a basinlike cavity for the white, elliptical eggs that will number seven or eight at the most and probably fewer. As each one is dropped she scrapes some earth over it. When she has expelled the final one, she covers the entire clutch with more earth. Then she quits the nest, and starts in on another summer of continual rambling.

Some three months later the eggs hatch. The young turtles that push their way up to the surface measure not quite an inch in diameter. Newly hatched turtles occasionally hibernate soon after breaking out of their shells, and even without eating. Such turtles, and also those that do not hibernate immediately, are nourished by the yolks of the eggs from which they hatched. The yolks are attached to the undersides of the lower shells, and provide food until the hatchlings are ready to eat—a matter of days if they do not hibernate immediately but a matter of months if they hibernate before eating.

When a young turtle starts foraging, an earthworm is likely to be its first food. Since it has no teeth, a turtle has its own peculiar way of eating. The edge of each sharp jaw has a covering of horny plates. The lower jaw is slightly smaller than the upper. This permits the one to fit inside the other, thus allowing the turtle to shear off its food in snippets. Each of these bits is swallowed whole. Before swallowing, a turtle sometimes mashes a bit of food against the roof of its mouth with the tongue. This helps to "tenderize" the food so that it can be swallowed more easily.

In order to drink, the box turtle must go right into the water. When the turtle is somewhat awash, it stretches out its neck as far as possible, then opens its mouth so that the water can trickle in. Though this turtle is terrestrial it can swim, and often seeks water during prolonged droughts.

As a hatchling and as a juvenile the box turtle spends much of its time in hiding. This is its only means of defense, for the shell is not sufficiently hard to protect it against skunks, crows, and other flesh-eating predators. For the first five or six years of its life, it grows ½ to ¾ inch a year. Later the annual growth rate is ¼ inch. This growth continues until the length of the shell is 5 or 6 inches—the size of a full-grown box turtle.

Whether young or old, the box turtle is plagued by two external parasites. One is the common North American chigger, whose specific name is *irritans;* the other is a bot fly. Neither parasite seems to trouble this turtle to any great extent.

By the time it is six years old, the box turtle's shell is hard enough to provide the necessary protection. Now it is free to wander over a home range. This wandering may continue each summer for eighty years or even longer. An eastern box turtle discovered in 1935 by Billy Johnson near Hope Valley, Rhode Island, had "1844" scratched on its lower shell.

According to the United Nations Educational, Scientific and Cultural Organization, the longest-lived turtle species are those found in the Galápagos and the Seychelles Islands. These huge land turtles, weighing 500 to 600 pounds, normally live 100 to 150 years. Though some specimens have been reported as having lived 200 years, the verified maximum life span is 152 years.

Land turtles have been put to an odd social usage, and together with other species have been the subjects of an unusual psychological study.

The mid-nineteenth century in Turkey has been called the Tulip Period. This era was so named because the Turkish people were extremely devoted to tulip gardens. In order to enjoy them after dark, they employed an unusual form of night lighting. In and around Ankara, tortoises bearing lighted candles were released so they could wander through the tulip gardens.

The electrical potential of turtle and tortoise ears was the subject of a paper read at a meeting of the Eastern Psychological Association held in Atlantic City in April 1956. The report stated that the turtle's ear is essentially a low-frequency instrument. Its sensitivity falls off rapidly beyond 1,000 cycles or the C two octaves above middle C. As a result of this low frequency, it was concluded, "the voice of the turtle must be a deep voice if other turtles can hear it."

GOPHER TORTOISES
Gopherus

Throughout that region of the United States known as the Southwest there are fewer than twenty species of turtles. Other than the box turtle, only two of these may be considered truly dry-land species. One, the desert tortoise (*Gopherus agassizi*), is found in the southern parts of California, Arizona, and Nevada—some of the driest country in the entire Southwest. The other, the smaller Texas or Berlandier's tortoise (*G. berlandieri*) is restricted to southern Texas and the adjacent states in Mexico. This environment is not subjected to absolute desert conditions.

The desert tortoise is distinguished by a brown upper shell that is high-domed and a lower shell that has a heart-shaped projection at the front. The hind feet are thick and stumpy and similar in shape to those of an elephant. The forefeet have five claws, which are long, blunt, and inward-turning.

One indication that spring has come to the desert is the appearance of this tortoise. It usually emerges from hibernation in March, after having spent three months in a burrow of its own digging, or in some convenient crevice deep enough to protect it from extreme cold. During unusually hot weather the desert tortoise also retires to its burrow or some natural retreat.

The room to which the desert tortoise retreats to escape unfavorable weather is usually three feet beneath the floor of the desert. But the single tunnel by which this room is reached may be as long as eight feet. Upon emerging from its subterranean chamber in the spring, the movements of the desert tortoise are deliberate. It has to shake off the lethargy of hibernation before it becomes fully active. Once it is again in condition for its active season, it starts out on a foraging trip.

Most such trips occur early in the morning or late in the afternoon. A desert tortoise also searches for food on an overcast day or immediately after a rain. And those of the Mojave Desert forage at noon, keeping in the shade as they do so.

The desert tortoise is herbivorous, and makes it way over a home range in a hobbledehoy manner as it searches for vegetation. If the sand is neither too hard nor too soft, the foraging turtle usually leaves faint tracks that may show a hint of a tail drag.

In its wayward course around its sandy, cactus-studded environment a desert tortoise may pause to shear off a bit of prickly pear, then wander on to take a nip of the beavertail cactus. These and other plants help to furnish a part of the moisture the tortoise needs to maintain life.

During the spring rains, when the deserts bloom, the tortoise drinks from any convenient puddle. Some water goes directly to the stomach, but some also goes into a bladderlike container that lies beneath the top shell. This reservoir is drawn upon when no water is available. And during prolonged dry spells this turtle prevents dehydration to some degree by passing little or no water. It is just possible that some water is manufactured by the tortoise itself through oxidation of its foods—an internal chemical process compounding hydrogen and oxygen to form water.

If the desert tortoise which emerges in the spring is a full-grown male, his hemispherical shell may measure 13 inches from front to rear. At some time during one of his foraging trips, the male is sure to meet a female, whose shell is slightly larger than his. If no other male is near by, a courtship starts at once, with the male gently nipping the fleshy parts of the female.

A courtship is sometimes interrupted by the arrival of another male. This means a fight. The males stand as high as they can on their broad legs, emitting sounds similar to the hiss of steam escaping from a valve on a radiator. The males nip at one another, and also push against each other with the horny front plates of the lower shell. The winner is the male that flips its adversary over on its back. Then the victor and the female leave the arena before mating.

In June the female is ready to deposit her eggs. She uses her hind legs to scoop out a shallow hole at the entrance to her burrow. She expels six eggs—round, white, and hard—which she carefully covers with sand. She then smooths the sand over the clutch so the spot appears as undisturbed as the surrounding area. The eggs incubate during the hot, dry weeks of the desert summer, while the parents of the turtles-to-be are estivating.

At about the time the male and the female arouse from their summer sleep, the eggs hatch. The young desert tortoises work their way up out of the sand—six new arrivals in a hot, dry land, dotted with cacti and patrolled at night by elf owls—tiny desert creatures that nest in the saguaro.

The third of the gopher tortoises is G. *polyphemus* of the Southeast. It ranges from southern South Carolina to central Florida, and westward along the Gulf coast as far as southeastern Texas.

This species is a great digger, and burrows a tunnel in the sandy soil that may be 15 or 20 feet in length. A burrow opening matches the size and shape of the digger, for it is an oval measuring 6 by 9 inches. You can usually identify the burrow opening of the gopher tortoise by the scooped-out earth at the entrance—an entrance that offers safety to the black snake, the gopher frog, the burrowing owl, and the raccoon. For these animals try to dodge predators by caching themselves in the burrow of the gopher tortoise.

DIAMONDBACK TERRAPIN
Malaclemys terrapin

". . . never intended for vulgar palates."
New York *Morning Dispatch*,
May 7, 1912

The Gridiron Club of Washington, D. C., is sometimes referred to as "the world's most famous dining club." The majority of its members are newspapermen, and each year they hold a banquet during which a variety show is staged. For decades one of the dishes on the menu of this annual affair has been terrapin à la Maryland. In recent years the Club has found it more and more difficult to secure enough terrapins for the nearly 550 guests. For this turtle of salt and brackish water and coastal mud flats is not nearly so numerous as it used to be.

During the years when terrapin was in the greatest demand, the annual catch in the Chesapeake Bay area alone amounted to as much as 90,000 pounds. Since the average weight of the diamondback is two pounds, this meant that in a single year 45,000 of these turtles were caught and shipped to market. Each sold for nearly six dollars.

Fortunately, the culinary demand for the diamondback lessened. This was one aid in helping to save another North American animal from possible extinction. Legal protection in the form of closed seasons in some states was also a benefit. In 1923 North Carolina in cooperation with the old U. S. Biological Survey banned all killing of the diamondback for five years. Young diamondbacks in Maryland and North Carolina are currently protected by law.

The diamondback terrapin has a dark olive carapace patterned in concentric rings or ridges and bordered by plates hollow in the center, and lighter in color than the shell proper. The plastron is deep yellow, relieved by rows of black dots and etched with dark horizontal bands. The head, legs, and other exposed fleshy parts are sprinkled with black dots.

The size of a full-grown diamondback depends upon the sex. The female is larger than the male. By the time a female is five years of age, the length of her upper shell is nearly 5½ inches. As she ages her shell may enlarge until it measures as much as 7½ or even 8 inches for the southern species, slightly less for one in the North. The diamondback may live to be forty years old.

A female is ready to breed when she is five years old. Once a mating is consummated and the eggs are fertilized, she is ready to deposit her clutch in a nest made by scooping out a hole in some muddy bank. Here she deposits seven to twenty-three white eggs, with the average clutch containing twelve. The eggs hatch in about ninety days.

Upon hatching, a young diamondback is an inch long and may be light olive, dark brown, or a hue in between due to an admixture of the two colors. Sometimes the margin of the upper jaw of a newly hatched diamondback is lighter in color than the rest of the head. For their first winter of hibernation the young frequently use the hole in which they were hatched.

The combined ranges of the various diamondback terrapins is from Cape Cod, Massachusetts, south into Florida, then west along the shoreline of the Gulf of Mexico, into Texas as far as the mouth of the Rio Grande. Throughout this range the diamondback is found in salt and brackish waters and in rivers up to the limits of tidal flow. Its preference for this type of environment sets the diamondback apart from the terrapin in the genera *Pseudemys* and *Graptemys*—species that frequent fresh waters.

The diamondback floats for hours at a time in a vertical position. Staying upright with merely the tip of its snout out of the water is no trick at all. For the hind feet are broad and well-webbed, and by moving them in the fashion of a man treading water, the turtle drifts along with barely a ripple.

As it floats, it forages. Among the animals in its diet are various mollusks and shellfish. It also eats various seaweeds. All foods are taken under water and ground up by the powerful jaws before being swallowed.

The word *terrapin* is of Algonquin origin, and derives either from the Abnaki word *toarebe*, or the Lenape word *turupe*—both meaning "little turtle." The catch of the Lenapes' little turtle has declined since the days when the New York *Morning Dispatch* said terrapin was never intended for the vulgar palate. According to the U. S. Fish and Wildlife Service, the pounds of turtles taken during the late 1950's, and the market value of this poundage, were:

Diamondback Terrapin,
Malaclemys terrapin

	lbs.	
1959	14,000	$ 5,000
1958	16,000	4,000
1957	26,000	12,000
1956	29,000	10,000

The 1959 catch was primarily from the Chesapeake Bay area. Not all terrapins shipped to market are wild. At rearing stations these turtles are held in pens for nine years before they are ready to be marketed.

Map Turtle or Geographic Terrapin
Graptemys geographica

This turtle gets its common name because its shell markings are similar to those of the lines on a contour map. Among the dozen or so species and subspecies in the genus *Graptemys* the one known as the common map turtle has the widest distribution. It is found from the southern shores of the Great Lakes and the St. Lawrence River area, south through the drainage of the Mississippi River to Missouri, Kentucky, and Arkansas.

The contours on the carapace of a map turtle are outlined in faint yellow, with the color more distinct on the head and legs. The rear edge of the carapace is serrated—roughly edged—and this shell characteristic is an identifying mark. The male is usually smaller than the female, which may measure 9 to 12 inches in length. These turtles are easily scared, and take to the water at the slightest hint of danger.

Early in the summer the female leaves her usual habitat to come ashore. This sortie is generally in the morning. Once on land she begins to look for a spot where the earth is sufficiently soft to permit her to hollow out a flask-shaped nest. She then deposits ten to sixteen soft, white, elliptical eggs. As soon as the last one is expelled, she covers them, then hurries back to the water.

During its active season the map turtle, close relative of the diamondback terrapin, spends a great many hours in the sun. How much sun an individual turtle receives is a matter of speculation.

For these creatures frequently take their ease in layers. The first to have secured a spot in the sun may be the bottom one of several. Each sprawls with its forelegs dangling in front and its hind legs extended backward. And it is not unusual to see one with its elongated head pillowed on a clawed forefoot.

Long hours in the sun are interrupted when the map turtle quits its basking place to forage. The adult is largely herbivorous; it eats almost any part of whatever water plants grow in its particular habitat. But it will also eat crayfish, snails, clams, and other water animals. The jaws are equipped with sharp cutting edges and wide surfaces—surfaces which permit it to break the shells of mollusks and reach the meat inside. A young map turtle is primarily carnivorous, and feeds on all sorts of small water animals, including larval insects, snails, and worms.

As soon as the cool days and cooler nights of autumn curtail the activity of the map turtle, it seeks a place to hibernate. The choice of a hibernating spot for one group of these turtles sets them apart from the others throughout the range. For the map turtle of northern Illinois beds down for the winter in muskrat houses—dome-shaped structures with walls that are 4 to 12 inches thick. Protected by the insulation furnished by other members of its community, the map turtles of this part of the United States have additional security against winter weather. Others settle down in soft bottom mud or burrow into stream embankments. And occasionally some in a given population remain active—even during coldest winter weather.

PAINTED TURTLES
Chrysemys

Among the many symbols of the Plains Indians copied by the traveler-artist George Catlin is one of a turtle. This might well be a stylized drawing of the painted turtle, since the home range of one species includes Montana and neighboring regions, formerly Indian country. The species here is the western painted turtle (*Chrysemys picta belli*), the largest of the four in this group. It and the eastern, midland, and southern species frequent ponds in eastern Canada, the same kind of waters in much of the United States, and similar environments in northern Mexico.

The typical form of this turtle (*C. picta*) is most abundant in the Middle Atlantic states. Here you frequently find the painted turtle sunning on the end of a partly submerged log, or some other raftlike object that offers basking room and quick access to the water. Sometimes half a dozen of these turtles line the end of a log sticking out of a pond, where the yellow-green duckweed floats motionless on the surface and the strap-leaved cattails choke the shallows around the edges.

A sound alerts the basking turtles to danger. Although they have no external ears, they "hear" by means of the vibrations that travel as sound waves through the ground or the water. The vibration created by even a cautious footfall sends them plopping all helter-skelter into the water, to seek safety among the submerged plants. Once all vibrations cease, the turtles surface one by one, then resume their places in the sun when danger is past.

Probably these turtles are also able to sight danger. D. B. Casteel, writing in 1911 on "The Discriminative Ability of the Painted Turtle," told of test turtles which learned to distinguish between black and white lines, either horizontal or vertical. But what was really astonishing was the fact that they could also differentiate between lines of varying widths.

The painted turtle, known too as the pond turtle and sometimes as the painted terrapin, is easily identified. The flat, smooth carapace measures from 4 to 6 inches from end to end. It is black, brown, or dark olive, and the shields along the margins are marked with bright red or yellow-red. The undershell is such a bright yellow that it looks as if it had been freshly scrubbed.

It is not difficult to distinguish a young painted turtle from an old one. The red marks, half-moons, and irregular splotches on a young turtle are especially vivid, and there is a band of yellow on the back. The carapace of an older turtle has only faint red marks on the upper margins, though underneath this color is retained as long as it lives.

Any painted turtle is so thoroughly aquatic that it always eats under water. An omnivorous feeder, it eats all sorts of aquatic insects and their larvae, the young of frogs and toads, small fishes of various kinds, and a number of aquatic plants. During the early stages of its life, it is preyed upon by some members of the weasel family, by crows, and by some hawks and owls.

All painted turtles are excellent aquarium pets. The western is the longest-lived, with a record span of more than ten years. A painted turtle learns to accept food from your hand. It takes dabs of raw chopped beef or bits of fish from the tip of your finger, then submerges to eat. It also likes bits of lettuce or other tender parts of vegetables for browse.

The male, distinguished by a longer tail than that of the female, does the courting. As he approaches the female of his choice, he waves the long nails of his forefeet before her face, or even makes them vibrate by holding them against her face.

A mating is usually consummated so that a female is ready to lay her eggs during early summer. She comes ashore to deposit five to eight eggs—smooth, white, and soft-shelled. The preferred nesting spot seems to be near an old stump and close to the water.

When a young painted turtle breaks out of its shell, later in the summer, it is one inch long and nearly the same width. By the time it measures 3½ inches from end to end, this turtle has passed its fourth birthday and is ready to breed. From then on growth is much slower, with the size of the female always exceeding that of the male. One of the largest known painted turtles was a western species whose carapace was nearly 10 inches in length.

As a group these turtles act as scavengers in their communities, and as a group they have no market value because the flesh is considered of poor quality. They annoy fishermen by taking a baited hook—which seems to be an irresistible attraction, for the same turtle is often caught repeatedly by the same fisherman during an afternoon of angling. Apparently such behavior proves that "once hooked" does not make a painted turtle "twice shy." The arrival of cold weather puts a stop to this behavior, for the lowered temperatures force the painted turtle to hibernate deep in the bottom mud of its home water. Here it stays, barely alive, until some natural signal rouses it the following spring.

COOTERS and SLIDERS
Pseudemys

Among the eighteen species and subspecies of river turtles commonly called cooters and sliders is one of the few North American turtles that have increased in numbers. It is surprising that some should have done so, when you consider the polluted state of many waterways.

This turtle is the yellow-bellied turtle (*P. scripta scripta*), found from Virginia as far south as northern Florida and in southeastern Alabama. This species is an omnivorous feeder, and therefore probably a scavenger to some extent—possibly the reason for its increase while closely related species are less abundant or gone from parts of their ranges.

Another slider is the red-eared turtle (*P. s. elegans*), sometimes known as the elegant slider. This medium-sized turtle is distinguished by a red dash behind each eye, a decided contrast to its olive-brown shell. The males of this species are considerably darker in color than the females, and have much longer nails on the front feet.

The male red-eared turtle uses these long nails to woo a female. He tickles her chin or gently strokes her head during the initial stages of the courtship. This tickling and stroking occurs in the water, with the male swimming in front of the female and repeating his maneuver every few seconds until she succumbs. Shortly after the mating is consummated, the female leaves the water. On shore, she digs a hole in which she deposits eight to ten eggs. She carefully covers the clutch before returning to the water.

Not all clutches hatch, for bears and raccoons dig out the eggs and eat them, and another reptile, the king snake, also includes them in its diet. In turn the red-eared turtle feeds on the larval forms of aquatic insects, on fish, dead or alive, and on other animals and some plants.

From time to time fishery biologists make studies of turtles in relation to other animals of a community. Don Moss of the Alabama Department of Conservation has this to say about "The Effect of the Slider Turtle . . . on the Production of Fish in Farm Ponds":

The contents of 58 slider turtle stomachs that were trapped from various ponds in Central Alabama were analyzed and it was found that the food consisted approximately 80 per cent vegetable matter and 20 per cent animal matter. Filamentous algae made up approximately 45 per cent of the total diet while fish constituted less than 3 per cent.

SPOTTED TURTLE
Clemmys guttata

Some of the most colorful turtles in North America are the four categorized as pond turtles. One of these is the spotted turtle. The yellow-orange dots sprinkled on the shields of its smooth black carapace are reason enough for the name of this long-necked species. It is abundant on most of a range that includes the eastern part of southern Canada, and on south through the United States into northern Florida as well as west into parts of Wisconsin and Michigan.

Throughout this range the 3-to-5-inch spotted turtle frequents fresh-water pools and ponds, slow-moving small streams, and occasionally the brackish waters of coastal marshes. It is not completely water-bound, for it often wanders along a wooded stream bank. This wandering always takes place where there is plenty of dense ground cover, making the turtle difficult to spot.

Whether it forages on land or in the water, the spotted turtle is not doing any damage to what are known as "man's interests." Man, of course, is affecting the interests of the spotted turtle, what with the drainage of small water areas, the clearing and filling in of damp, wooded spots, and the building of summer-cottage colonies along small waterways.

Long before the season of summer cottages is at hand, the spotted turtle puts in its appearance. One such turtle is known to have come out of hibernation in southeastern New York on the second day of March. Undoubtedly the spotted turtle is a little sluggish when it emerges from its deep sleep.

The temperatures of the first warm spring days make it possible in time for the animal to overcome the lethargy of hibernation. Sometimes an unusually warm period in early spring rouses a turtle so that it comes out of hibernation, leaves the water, and makes a landfall. This may be fatal, for if it stays ashore too late in the day and the temperature drops unexpectedly, the early-out turtle becomes too sluggish to move, and is frozen in the mud. Later in the season, the cracked and broken shell of a dead turtle is testimony that here was one too adventuresome for its own good.

In the wild the spotted turtle forages for such insects as beetles and dragonflies and their larvae, for slugs, spiders, and tadpoles, and for bits of water plants. It eats all food under water. In the aquarium, it takes such foods as chopped beef, fish and shellfish, and bits of lettuce and other greens—all of which, again, are consumed under water.

When the mating season arrives the males fight among themselves; then individuals quit the jousting area to take off in pursuit of females. Each one seems to make an individual choice. Shortly after mating the female comes out of the water to lay two to four white eggs, elliptical in shape and measuring 1⅕ inches by ¾ inch. The eggs are buried in sandy spots, and if unmolested they hatch in about three months. At first a young spotted turtle has only a single dot on each black plate, but as it grows older, more dots appear. And in time they appear also on the legs and the tail.

The life expectancy of the spotted turtle is forty years or more. A mature, full-grown male always has a longer tail than the female. A male with an upper shell that measures nearly 4 inches in length has a tail 1⅞ inches long; a female of about the same size has a tail measuring only ¾ inch. The male has brown eyes, whereas those of the female are yellow.

The spotted turtle has shown an ability to find its way through a maze in order to reach food placed at the exit. So in addition to being one of our most colorful turtles, this species is apparently one of our smartest.

The spotted turtle has a number of close relatives among the pond turtles. One is the only fresh-water turtle of the Far West. This is the western pond turtle (*C. marmorata*), which with two subspecies ranges from southern Canada south along the Pacific coast and into northern Baja California. Though slightly larger than the spotted turtle, it is similar in its habits, and is addicted to sunning on logs and rocks.

Another of this group includes the bog turtle (*C. muhlenbergi*), formerly known as Muhlenberg's turtle. The bog turtle is distinguished by a black head and orange splotches above each temple. Its habits and behavior place it in an ecological niche between the spotted turtle and the wood turtle: it is not so completely aquatic as the first nor so attached to the land as the second.

The bog turtle likes narrow streams with clear water, bordered by numerous small marshy areas. It spends much of its time in the marshes, taking off for the water when alarmed, although at such a slow pace that it is easily caught. It eats either in or out of the water, and feeds on the tender parts of various plants and their fruits, on insects of all kinds, and on earthworms.

Though the range of the bog turtle is not extensive, you are likely to find it in New York, New Jersey, and Pennsylvania as far north as Lake George to the east and westward to the vicinity of Lakes Erie and Ontario. Farther east the range is from Rhode Island south into Maryland and Virginia and west to the mountainous parts of North Carolina.

How long the bog turtle will be a part of the North American wildlife community is uncertain. Peter Matthiessen has this to say about it in *Wildlife In America*:

[It] once occurred throughout the East, but the destruction of its swamps and sphagnum bogs through drainage has limited it to a few widely separated localities . . .

WOOD TURTLE
Clemmys insculpta

For lo! the winter is past, the rain is over and gone;
the flowers appear on the earth; the time of the singing
of the birds is come, and the voice of the turtle
is heard in our land.

Though this verse from the Song of Solomon refers to the turtle dove, it could apply equally well to the wood turtle. Most turtles are capable of little more than whispering sigh or an insignificant squeak. But both the male and the female of this species have whistling calls. That of the male has been described as a "distinct

but subdued note not unlike that of tea kettle." This call, however, has sufficient volume to carry a distance of thirty or forty
feet. The call of the female, on the other hand, is spoken of as
"merely a low whistle." Such sounding off is not confined to turtles
in the wild. Herpetologist Albert H. Wright kept a male that used
to whistle again and again at a female. This whistling may be some
sort of courting behavior—an attention attracting device, perhaps,
to tell the female that the male is nearby. In the wild such calling

Wood Turtle,
Clemmys insculpta

occurs in swampy areas, moist woods, or damp fields throughout
the Northeast and in the vicinity of the Great Lakes.

The reddish-orange or brick-red flesh of the wood turtle is considered good eating by many people. As a result it has been killed
in such numbers that it is scarce—so scarce in some areas that it is
now protected by law. Section 194 of the Conservation Law of
New York State reads: "Land turtles, box and wood turtles, and
tortoises shall not be taken, possessed, bought or sold."

Though the wood turtle is an omnivorous feeder, it has a liking
for what might be called the specialties of its home range. On this
preferred list are mushrooms, blackberries, strawberries, and rasp-
berries. It also eats tender plant parts, among which are sure to be the
young sprouts of wild asparagus and milkweed, and fallen fruits of
all kinds.

In his *Fieldbook of Natural History*, E. Laurence Palmer writes that the wood turtle "has the unusual ability to climb." So possibly it does not have to wait for fruits to become overripe and fall, but climbs to get such delicacies. Of course it also eats some animal food. Such food may be a part of its diet in spring when the wood turtle is likely to be found in the water, feeding on aquatic insects and other small water animals. But it is capable of going without food for almost a year, provided its skin is kept moist.

The wood turtle mates both in the spring and in the fall. The fertilized eggs are laid in clutches that may contain as few as two or as many as twelve. The female buries the round, white eggs in the sand during June and always about the same time—in the afternoon. The elements incubate the eggs, which produce young whose shells are nearly round and whose exposed fleshy parts are gray—so unexpected when you consider the bright-colored flesh of the adult. Perhaps this muted color helps to protect the turtlet during the interval it takes for the shell to harden.

The wood turtle makes a fine pet, though it does bite gently if annoyed for any length of time. The ideal terrarium is one with plenty of cover, a supply of favorite foods, and a temperature between 68° and 75° F.

The lengths of time wood turtles have lived in zoological parks varies greatly. One in the National Zoological Park in Washington, D. C., lived for nearly six years. Another in the London Zoological Gardens was in residence one hundred years, from 1839 to 1939.

Spiny Softshell Turtle
Trionyx ferox (Amyda ferox)

"Although so specialized in structure, the soft-shelled
turtles have been in this condition for a long time:
from the middle of the Cretaceous,
or perhaps a hundred million years."
Clifford H. Pope,
The Reptile World

The spiny softshell turtle is found in inland waters. Its greenish-brown carapace is nearly circular and practically flat. Because this is so, it is known as the "flapjack turtle," a name also applied to other members of the same genus.

The center of the upper shell of this turtle is hard in comparison with the soft, leathery margins. Black rings or circles are sprinkled liberally over its entire surface. The light green, soft undershell is unmarked and matches the head, legs, and short tail in color. The webbed feet have three claws. The narrow head, at the end of a long, snakelike neck, is equipped with jaws whose mandibles have the cutting edge of a well-honed straight razor. These jaws are concealed by folds of skin that give the creature a deceptively inoffensive appearance, for it can inflict a severe wound.

The spiny softshell is found on the soft bottoms of various waters throughout a great part of the United States, in a small area of northern Mexico, and in an equally small part of southern Canada. It is not found in the New England or Middle Atlantic states, in the Rocky Mountain region, or along the Pacific coast. And it never occurs in swift-moving forest streams or in those whose banks are densely wooded. In some places the range of this turtle coincides with that of the smooth, or spineless, softshell turtle (*T. muticus*), a little-known, smaller species. The water areas which the spiny softshell frequents vary with the species or subspecies.

Not a great deal is known about the life history and behavior of the spiny softshell turtle. Late in the spring or early in the summer the female quits the water. Her leavetaking is in the morning or early afternoon. She wanders around on webbed feet until she finds a nesting site to her liking. Here she digs in, using her hind legs to scoop out a nest that has the shape of a flask and a depth that depends upon the length of her legs. Some nests are as much as a foot deep. Once the nest is ready, she deposits her eggs—which are brittle, white, and spherical, measuring $1\frac{1}{10}$ inches in diameter. The clutch may number as few as ten or as many as twenty-five. Some females cover the eggs with the greatest of care, but others do not bother.

How long it takes for the eggs to incubate is unknown. It may be from two to ten months. On the most northerly parts of the range, the embryonic turtles probably overwinter in the shell and do not emerge until the spring of the next year. As soon as a young turtle breaks out of the shell, it makes directly for the water.

Spiny Softshell Turtle,
Trionyx ferox (*Amyda ferox*)

Anywhere on its range the spiny softshell turtle feeds on the small animals of its environment. The crayfish is the principal item of its diet. It also eats some soft parts of water plants, and a little dead or dying matter. All food is swallowed whole, after being scooped in with the aid of the forefeet.

The spiny softshell turtle and its close relative, the smooth or spineless softshell, are particularly agile and speedy swimmers. There is no record as to how fast the spiny softshell swims, but the smooth or spineless is known to have cut through the water at ten miles an hour.

The smooth or spineless softshell turtle has little or no market value. But the spiny species is considered excellent eating, and consequently it is trapped. A large adult furnishes a surprising amount of meat, for some measure as much as 13 inches in length and weigh as much as seven pounds.

These thoroughly aquatic turtles are likely to be most active when the temperature of their surroundings is 79° F. They stay under water for hours at a time. They are able to do so because as they submerge, little valvelike processes in the nostrils automatically close. At other times the softshell turtle settles down in shallow water with only its head above the surface. And at still other times this turtle suns itself on any convenient log or rock, looking not unlike a flapjack on a griddle.

These, then, are some of our North American turtles. They are only a few of the world's two hundred-odd kinds of turtles, whose ancestors were on earth during the Triassic period, twenty million years or so ago. The ancestor of some North American turtles, the Chelonians, is known scientifically as *Archelon*. The remains of this turtle were found in fossil form in what is now South Dakota. *Archelon* had an overall length of 12 feet, and may have weighed as much as a ton. Despite its present abundance of turtles, the United States has no such giant forms as *Archelon* today.

Nevertheless the turtles written about in this book, as well as such others as the cooter (*Pseudemys floridana*) and the chicken turtle (*Deirochelys reticularia*), and the various regional forms, are worth study, for surprisingly there is much to be learned about even those turtles we consider common. And I believe you will find that turtle behavior is both fascinating and puzzling.

One fall as I walked from north to south in Gambril State Park, six miles northwest of Frederick, Maryland, I noted that every box turtle I saw was moving in the same direction. Each was leaving the marshy land on the east side of the rutted road for the less marshy land on the west side. Was this a seasonal movement in search of spots in which to hibernate? (It was still early in the season, and still warm enough for me to go without a jacket.) Or had some other cause motivated it? To this day I have not determined the reason for this east-west movement.

CROCODILIANS

In the United States the crocodilians are represented by two species. One is the American crocodile and the other is the American alligator. Both are reptiles, both are amphibious in habits, and both are found in the same part of the country, though the alligator has the more extensive range of the two.

These two species, together with those in South America, Asia, and Africa, are direct descendants of the crocodilians that existed during the Mesozoic era, the Age of Reptiles, which began about 200 million years ago. As such they are of particular interest, for they represent a time in the world's history from which there are few surviving forms.

The alligator and the crocodile are massive, heavy-scaled reptiles that belong to the order Crocodilia, a name that has replaced Loricata. The former name derived from a Latin word meaning "protected by plates." The family name of these two animals is Crocodylidae, which in the singular (*crocodilus*) means "crocodile." Some authorities place the alligator in a family of its own, the Alligatoridae.

Close allies of the crocodile and the alligator are the flat-snouted gavial of India and Malaya, and the brightly colored caiman known in South America as the *jacare*. Though some of the alligators, crocodiles, caimans, and gavials may be considered harmless, none can be called gentle—a word used by William Blake in describing the crocodile.

Blake's use of "gentle" was in connection with the so-called crocodile bird (*Pluvianus aegyptius*) found in Africa. This plover-like bird alights on the crocodile's back in search of parasitic insects, sometimes even enters the animal's open mouth in search of flies and other insects. It is reasonable to assume that the crocodile knows a good thing when it has it, and is therefore gentle with *P. aegyptius*, if not with any other creatures.

AMERICAN CROCODILE
Crocodylus acutus

The tears shed by anyone pretending sorrow are known as "crocodile tears." People used to believe that the crocodile cried while devouring human prey, or else that it made a weeping sound to lure such prey within its reach.

Now it has been established that crocodiles do cry, but not as a lure or as a sign or hypocrisy. The kidneys of these scaly-skinned creatures cannot dispose of all the salt intake. To overcome this handicap, nature has provided glands in the head which extract salt and then pass it in the form of tears.

The ancestor of the tear-shedding crocodile was once found in various areas of what is now the United States—a fact proved by positive identification of fossil crocodiles. A new territory for this animal was reported by *Science News Letter* in June 1962. Two students at the University of Oregon, at Eugene, found the first fossil crocodile ever discovered west of the Rocky Mountains. This specimen, probably measuring 8 feet in length, was in rock 45 to 60 million years old.

Today if you wish to see a crocodile in the United States, you will have to travel to the southernmost part of Florida. Here, amid watery, subtropical surroundings, is the only spot in the country where this animal still exists, on a range shaded by mangrove trees.

This animal is sometimes referred to as the North American crocodile; but the designation "American" is better. For this same species has a range east to the West Indies, south through Central America, and along the coast of Ecuador.

The American crocodile is easily recognized for the animal it is. You can never mistake it for its close relative, the American alligator, a fresh-water creature. Although both are large, have long tails, and look like giant lizards, the crocodile is slimmer, with a long, pointed head and a semicircular bulge above each yellow-green eye. It has short, bowed-looking legs ending in clawlike feet. There is a fringed webbing between the toes of the hind feet that helps in swimming. The skin is tough, made so by many small bony plates and a series of skin scales of a horny consistency. The teeth are of varying sizes; each is as sharp and strong as a shoemaker's awl, and is set in an individual socket along the outer edge of the jaw. The long fourth tooth of the lower jaw shows when the mouth is closed, whereas the corresponding tooth of the alligator is concealed in a cavity.

The crocodile is one of the most aquatic of reptiles, using its feet and its long, strong tail to propel itself through the water. When it floats, it folds its forelegs back against the body; then to move it lashes its tail from side to side. This swimming method sends the animal forward on or near the surface in much the same way a tadpole wriggles along.

The crocodile's long, tapering tail is also a weapon of defense. The animal can maneuver it with such dexterity and force as to administer a killing blow. Unlike the crocodiles of Africa and India, the American species is not considered a man-eater.

Even in crocodile country it is not easy to catch sight of one. The animal is endowed with excellent hearing. Long before you or your guide are aware of a crocodile, it is aware of you. The sounds

American Crocodile, *Crocodylus acutus*

of your movements, no matter how stealthy, are picked up immediately by the animal's sensitive ears. And by the time you come along, the crocodile has removed itself to a favorite water hole, a deep place in one of the many fresh or brackish waterways that crisscross the animal's range.

The crocodile uses such a hole as its lair. Frequently this is beneath a shelving bank, and here the animal lurks for its prey—birds, fishes, crayfish, crabs, turtles, and other live animals. In addition to the lair, the crocodile uses certain spots along a waterway for basking in the sun.

If you happen to catch sight of a basking animal, you could judge its age by the color of the skin. A young one has a distinctly greenish cast, with a number of black markings. One that is half grown or in the first stages of adulthood is the color of a green olive, whereas an old animal is a uniform gray.

The size to which American crocodiles grow varies with individuals and their whereabouts on the range. One of the largest on record measured 14 feet 2 inches, exclusive of 4 inches of missing tail. This specimen was a male. It was captured in 1875 in Arch Creek, a stream in the vicinity of Biscayne Bay. The finding of this specimen and a second one by naturalist Dr. William T. Hornaday and a companion proved for the first time the existence of true crocodiles in the United States. The record length for a crocodile in the United States is 15 feet. The record for a specimen from South America is 23½ feet. And the photographer and writer V. J. Stanek states it is not uncommon to see crocodiles along the coast of Ecuador measuring as much as 22 feet.

As a rule the female is not so long as the male. The measurements of one female at the New York Zoological Park were:

Overall length	10 feet	2½ inches
Tail	4 feet	9 inches
Girth	3 feet	11 inches
Weight		280 pounds

Captive females deposit as many as thirty eggs to a clutch, whereas wild ones may lay clutches of forty or more. The eggs are expelled in a "nest" of vegetable matter that makes a good-sized mound. Each egg measures 3 to 3½ inches in length and 2 inches in diameter.

The shell is not easy to break, for it is thicker than that of a duck's egg.

Humidity, the heat of the sun and of the decaying vegetable matter all play a part in the incubation of the eggs. When it breaks out of its shell the average wild crocodile is no more than 8 inches long, and it weighs about 9 ounces.

Not all eggs in a clutch hatch, so the potential crocodile population is limited from the start. And mortality among young crocodiles is great. Even though the young stay in shallow waters for protection, many are caught by turtles, fishes, and other predators. From a single clutch only a few reach old age, and today this is seldom more than twenty-five years. Before these reptiles were hunted so relentlessly, many lived for more than fifty years. One individual of a different species is known to have had a longer life span than most crocodiles today. This was a marsh or mugger crocodile (*C. palustris*), an Asiatic species that lived for thirty-one years. Despite the name *mugger* and its connotations, this species is classed with the American crocodile as one of the non-man-eating kind.

The American crocodile is immortalized in a folk-art wood carving. During the Seventh Annual Antiques Show held in January 1962, a pine-wood crocodile was on exhibit at Washington's Shoreham Hotel. According to David Good, a collector of such items, this figure, priced at $585, was once owned by President John Quincy Adams as a poolside ornament.

AMERICAN ALLIGATOR
Alligator mississipiensis

"Behold him rushing forth from the flags and reeds."
WILLIAM BARTRAM (1791)

For centuries Okefenokee Swamp in southeastern Georgia has been a sanctuary for the American alligator. The Swamp is a primitive area of shallow waters and land hummocks, of old cypress, gum, and bay trees, of odd aquatic plants such as the "never-wet," whose yellow spikes are reflected in glassy waters where alligators float, seemingly as lifeless as logs. And each spring, as naturalist

William Bartram wrote, "The shores and forests resound his dreadful roar."

Though Bartram wrote of the alligators he saw and heard during the 1790's as he paddled down the St. James River in southeast Florida, his comment applies to alligators anywhere on their range. in North America. Formerly this long-tailed, round-snouted reptile was to be found in coastal swamps and rivers from Albemarle Sound in North Carolina to the tip of Florida, and westward into Texas as far as the mouth of the Rio Grande.

The range is now much more restricted, and the animal is not nearly so numerous as in Bartram's time. When the Naturalist was exploring subtropical North America, he noted that "the alligators were in such incredible numbers, and so close together from shore to shore, that it would have been easy to have walked across on their heads, had the animals been harmless."

Nearly a century and three-quarters after Bartram visited Florida, the American alligator was in danger and listed as rare. Today, because most "alligator states" have enacted legislation to protect them, alligators are not so scarce. And the federal government has established refuges where the 'gator is safe from unlicensed hide hunters and from those people who shoot at anything alive merely for the sake of shooting.

One refuge providing sanctuary for the alligator is Delta National Wildlife Refuge in Louisiana. Here a tract of more than 48,000 acres provides the alligator with the environment necessary for its well-being: a coastal marsh crisscrossed by numerous waterways, an abundance of aquatic and other food, sunny spots for basking, and areas where the female can build a nest for her eggs.

A century ago the alligator frequently measured at least 15 feet from tip of snout to tip of tail. Fifty years ago the average length was 14 feet. Now one of these animals is considered large if its overall length is as much as 12 feet. One caught at Delta in 1957 caused a sensation because it measured 13½ feet. Seemingly as habitat decreases, the length to which the 'gator grows also decreases.

The amphibious alligator has managed to survive despite a dwindling range and more than two centuries of unrestricted hunting. Before 1800 there was no large-scale killing of 'gators. But from

1800 until the early 1900's, millions of these reptiles were killed each year. Today a limited number of 'gators are harvested legally each year, with the hides selling by the foot at prices varying from $1.25 to $2.50.

The alligator received its common name from the Spaniards. While they were exploring Florida in search of treasure and the Fountain of Youth, they saw their first 'gator and called it *el largarto*, "the lizard." In time the Spaniards' phrase became the English *alligator*—a name also used for the species in China, the only other place in the world where these reptiles are found.

Today the scientific name of the order to which the alligator belongs is Crocodilia. Once the name of the order was Loricata, which was derived from the Latin word *lorica*, whose literal meaning is "a corselet of thongs." And the hide of the alligator is in truth a corselet, for on the back are row after row of sharply ridged bony plates, and the abdomen, legs, and tail are protected by leathery shields.

The alligator is further distinguished by short, seemingly bowed legs that end in clawed feet. A fringed webbing between the claws connects them for nearly half their length. The alligator has a tail less flattened vertically than that of the crocodile, and can also be distinguished from its close relative by its greater girth and more massive skull. The skull and the girth combine to make the alligator a heavier animal than C. *acutus*. And at night, a 'gator's eyes shine ruby-red through the dark, the reason for its regional name "Old Fire Eyes."

The jaws of the alligator, with eighty large and small teeth implanted at the outer edges, are powerful. According to Frank M. Lane, author of *Nature Parade*, a trapped alligator bit down so hard on a flat piece of two-inch steel that "the ninth tooth of each side of its upper jaw was driven right through the bony top of the jaw, and the hollow ends of the tooth protruded above the bone." To unclamp the jaws of a 'gator is nearly impossible, although a man can close the jaws and hold them closed with one hand.

When alligators mate, it is the female who instigates the courtship and who is also the one to carry it through to its natural conclusion. How she determines which one of the bellowing males is to be her

American Alligator,
Alligator mississipiensis

mate is a secret known only to the alligator. But once a selection is made, a female starts a courtship that is arduous, persistent, and painstaking.

The wooing takes place in the water. Sometimes the female swims under the male, blowing bubbles to attract his attention. At other times she climbs upon his back, and pats or strokes him with her forefeet. These tactics may bring almost immediate results or last as long as a week.

Whether a short courtship indicates a young, inexperienced male and a week-long wooing denotes an old, experienced bull is a matter for conjecture. But whether the wooing is short or long, the male finally succumbs and mating is consummated.

A female brings as much zeal to her nest-building as she does to her courtship. A nest is usually built as near water as possible, and in the immediate vicinity of the female's den—a good-sized dugout in a stream bank with an entrance below water level. Her first move is to clear the nest area of all growths. She does this by shearing off some plants with a scissorlike movement of the jaws, clamping others between her jaws and yanking them out by the roots, and leveling still others by mashing them to the ground with her heavy body.

Next she maneuvers the torn-up vegetation, and any natural trash she may find, into a pile centered in the cleared area. This takes a bit of doing, for she has to haul into place by mouth, shove with snout, or push tail-end to. Once the material is in place she works it into a tightly packed mound, then levels off the top.

Now the female is ready to make a place to receive the clutch of eggs, that may number as few as ten or as many as one hundred. Probably the average clutch is thirty-five to fifty. She hollows the center by slowly pinwheeling her cumbersome body, with forelegs braced against the edge of the nest, and pushing backwards with first one hind foot and then the other. By the time she has made a complete circle, she has created a reasonably deep cavity.

The hollow is then filled with mud and underwater plants. To get this fill the female makes numerous trips to and from the waterway that flows through her territory—a stretch of a mile, possibly two at the greatest, along the stream in which she spends most of her time. When the large hollow is well filled, she does some additional smoothing of the mound before making a second, smaller cavity. Now she is ready to lay her eggs—which are similar in shape to those laid by a hen but slightly longer and narrower.

As soon as the last egg is deposited, the female covers the clutch with material pulled from the nest, and with more mud and aquatic plants hauled from the water. She tamps all this down with her belly and then crawls around and around on the nest until she has molded it into a cone-shaped affair. Now her work is complete. She has fashioned a natural incubator, in which organic decay provides much of the heat necessary to hatch the eggs. The heat from the sun and the humidity of the environment will also help.

A female stays within the vicinity of the nest until the eggs hatch. If the mud becomes dry, she leaves the water and crawls around on the nest to dampen it while her body is still wet. She will drive a man or other animal away, whipping her tail at the invader; on occasion a female has been known to charge, running as a lizard runs, with body raised as much above the ground as the short legs permit.

A nest over which a female stands guard is rarely approached by the raccoon, for this animal is afraid of the snapping jaws and the whipping tail. Apparently the black bear is, too. It never engages in direct combat with a female whose eggs are incubating, though in water deep enough for swimming a black bear has been known to worst an attacking 'gator, by coming up beneath it and clawing it on the underside from snout to tail.

The alligator is unique among reptiles because it is so noisy. The half-grown creature moos like a calf; the old 'gators bellow like bulls. Even before the young are out of the eggs, they grunt like so many piglets. As soon as the female hears them, she rushes to the nest and rips open the top, freeing her offspring.

At the time of hatching the length of the American alligator is not quite 8 inches and its weight is no more than two ounces at most. As soon as it is freed from the nest, it scuttles to the nearest water—whose temperature may be as much as 80° F. This much heat is exactly what the young animal needs for steady growth.

Cool or cold water retards growth and seems to cause a loss of appetite. A drought also affects the alligator to the extent that the animal estivates, burying itself deep in the mud where it remains inactive until rains bring the environment back to normal. And when winter comes the 'gator hibernates, passing this season in a state characterized by a greatly lowered metabolism.

During this quiescent interval, the oxygen consumption of the alligator, or of any other hibernating animal for that matter, may fall to $\frac{1}{30}$ or even to $\frac{1}{100}$ of the normal rate. The heartbeat decreases until the rate is only a few beats each minute, and the respiration is infrequent.

A recently hatched 'gator starts feeding at once. It eats various small fishes and many other small aquatic animals. In turn a young 'gator is preyed upon by others of its kind, and by various large fishes including the bony-scaled gar with its beaklike snout. The snouts of all gars, including the species known as the alligator gar (*Lepisosteus spatula*), are filled with teeth of varying sizes, on which prey can be impaled.

The young 'gator and its predator, the gar, have similar backgrounds. The 'gator is a descendant of a race of animals that lived during the Mesozoic—an era when dinosaurs, marine and flying reptiles, and ganoid fishes were abundant. The gar is a survivor of another ancient, primitive animal group, the ganoid fishes—fishes having hard scales of bone overlaid with an enamel-like finish. These fishes came into being during the Triassic—an era when rocks were mostly red sandstone and when fishes as we know them did not exist. And so the study of the 'gator and the gar enables us to have some idea of two groups of animals that existed millions of years ago.

During its first days in the water, a 'gator is protected from predatory males by the female, who drives a bull away with as much energy as she earlier used to attract him. And during the first three years of its life, a 'gator must play hide-and-seek to survive. Only by hiding in shallows is it able to escape the predators who seek it.

By the time a 'gator is three years old it can defend itself against most predators. At this age it measures nearly 3 feet and weighs 14 pounds or a trifle more. At six years its length is usually 6 feet. This measurement is based on records kept on marked alligators living in the wild. And it is during the sixth year that males begin to increase in size more rapidly than females.

As it turns ten, the overall length of a male is at least 9 feet—
perhaps slightly more—and its weight is 250 pounds. A female is
usually two feet shorter and seldom weighs more than 115 pounds.
The oldest wild American alligator we know of lived fifty-six years.
Though this age record is not documented, an American alligator on
display at the Jardin des Plantes in Paris is supposed to have had the
record life span for a captive. It is said to have died when it was
eighty-five years old, and rumor has it that all Paris mourned its
passing with genuine tears.

A fully grown 'gator has an enormous appetite. It eats a variety
of live prey and occasionally consumes such indigestible items as
pop bottles, chunks of wood, and shotgun shells. It feeds upon
waterfowl of all species, coming in beneath the birds as they paddle
around. An alligator nabs a bird with its jaws, drags it beneath the
surface, and holds it there until it drowns. The 'gator itself is in no
danger of drowning at this time, for it raises its tongue in such a
way that any inflow of water is blocked, and valves in the ears and
nostrils close so tightly that no seepage is possible.

Before the alligator can swallow its prey, it must surface and
thrust its head clear of the water. A bird the size of a teal or a ruddy
duck can be swallowed whole. It is digested by gastric juices strong
enough to burn your hand or any other exposed flesh.

Prey too large to be ingested at one gulp is shaken violently until
it is torn apart, then swallowed piecemeal. Two alligators sometimes
work together in pulling apart large animals such as hogs and deer
—which have been whipped by the powerful tail from streamside
into the water. A 'gator often waits beneath a tree when the young
of egrets or herons are in the nest. Such a wait is likely to be worth
its while, for many a down-covered nestling tumbles from, or is
shoved out of, the nest and drops into the water, where the waiting
'gator snaps it up.

The alligator can be an on-the-spot aid in management of marshes.
That part of the animal's range along the Gulf coast is an area where
sawgrass thrives. This semitropical plant, known to botanists as
Cladium jamaicensis, has leaves edged with sharp teeth. And where
it grows in profusion even trappers and hunters hesitate to work
their way in among the tall, dense stands.

Here and there throughout this sharp-edged jungle the rough-skinned 'gator roots out enough sawgrass to make itself a hole. In so doing it is responsible for creating the only open water in vast stretches of this coastal country. Thus the holes the 'gator makes here and elsewhere on its range are a start in creating better habitat for various fresh-water fishes and some waterfowl. One of these is the carnivorous mottled duck (*Anas fulvigula*), a species similar in appearance to the black duck, and one that feeds on such other members of its community as crayfish, snails, and various aquatic insects.

During 1949 biologists Leroy Giles and Vandiver Childs of the United States Fish and Wildlife Service made a study of the alligator at Sabine National Wildlife Refuge in Louisiana. Among other findings, they turned up further evidence that alligators prey on minks, muskrats, and otters. But the biologists also discovered that a large population of alligators meant an equally large population of muskrats—an indication, apparently, that alligators create habitat suitable for the fur-bearer.

Another service the alligator furnishes its community is in the control of turtles. According to *Life In The Everglades*, by Alexander Sprunt, Jr., "Where the alligator occurs is usually good fishing, for the turtles are kept under some natural control."

Both young and old alligators are exploited commercially. The young 'gator, whose black or dark brown hide is crisscrossed with yellow, is sold as a pet. The old animals, black or dull gray, are hunted in various ways because the hide is used in the manufacture of belts, wallets, handbags, shoes, and suitcases. Not all alligators become wearing apparel or traveling or clothing accessories. Some are made into soup; the Seminoles consider this a delicacy and the demand is usually greater than the supply. Some people like alligator meat. The part most frequently used is the muscle at the end of the tail. This meat, white and boneless, is said to have the flavor of frogs' legs. It does not have the strong, musky odor evident in the living creature. As an old bull roars, scent glands beneath the surface of the chin open like so many tiny jets to emit a fluid whose odor may be noticed miles away.

PART II

Amphibians: BOTH IN THEIR
LOVE AND HUNGER THEY ARE
ESPECIALLY ACTIVE IN THE
TWILIGHT.

New Standard Encyclopedia

Someone has called the amphibians a defeated group of animals. This remark is rather apt because not all of these four-footed creatures have been able to complete their transition from one element, water, to another, land. In her *Handbook of Nature Study*, Anna Botsford Comstock comments on the peculiarities of amphibians by saying, "While there are exceptions to the general rule, and great variations to the life habits of these animals, it may be said that they are fitted to spend certain periods of their lives on land and other periods in water."

The ancestors of today's "defeated animals" formed a large group of vertebrates on earth during the late Paleozoic. Many spent the greater part of their lives in water; but a few, as the result of interplay of environment and selection, stayed more and more on land, developing stronger and larger legs to help them get about in their new environment. Then, as the Carboniferous drew to a close, the reptiles became dominant. Now the amphibians were out-ranked.

Today only three orders of amphibians exist: the frogs and the toads, the tailless amphibians of the order Anura; the newts and the salamanders, the tailed amphibians of the order Caudata; and the caecilians, the wormlike, legless creatures of the order Apoda. These remnant animals, usually distinguished by a smooth, moist, and scaleless skin, are cold-blooded and backboned. They occupy a place in the animal kingdom between the fishes and the reptiles. A great many of them live up to the name of their class, Amphibia, in that they lead a double life—a period or periods in fresh water and intervals on land. Amphibians that do not start life in water or those that do not return to this element from time to time still require plenty of moisture.

Some amphibians retain gills throughout their lives, but most are distinguished by these organs only during their water-breathing stage. Then through changes in form and structure, the meta-morphosis, they become lung-breathing animals in adult form. As adults some make no environmental change, but remain in the water where they hatched from eggs. Others make a change, coming out on land where they spend the better part of their lives.

All amphibians have moist skins through which they absorb oxygen. Except for some toads, they are usually found where there is plenty of moisture—a necessary environmental situation, for they cannot stand dryness. In addition to their preference for moist areas, most amphibians like warm regions. Some, however, are found in temperate climates and on ranges that extend far to the north. One such is the wood frog (*Rana sylvatica*); it reaches or perhaps even crosses the Arctic Circle. Among the known amphibians, only the frogs and the toads have worldwide distribution. Most of the salamanders are confined to Europe and North America. Here is the distribution of these creatures throughout the world and their abundance by continent:

1. Tropical America
2. India
3. Africa
4. Australia
5. North America
6. Europe

In North America the tracks of some of the continent's first amphibians are in fossilized form in the region of the Grand Canyon of the Colorado. They are in a type of rock known as the Supai formation, a combination of red sandstone and shale named for the Havasupai. They were basket-weaving Indians who lived in the area. Today about one hundred Havasupai, an agricultural people, live in Havasu Canyon in Grand Canyon National Park, Arizona. The animal life in the Park's almost 1,100 square miles includes five North American amphibians.

FROGS AND TOADS

The frogs and the toads, the tailless amphibians (Anura), are a noisy lot. These squat creatures with long hind legs are given to barking, booming, and braying, as well as to chirping, peeping, and trilling. Throughout the world some two thousand frogs and toads produce these sounds, with ninety-odd species and subspecies making their share of the animal noises in the United States and Canada. Among this array is the smallest vertebrate in North America—the shiny brown chorus frog. The males of this species measure slightly less than ½ inch in length. In order to appreciate how tiny this species is, you must see it near a bullfrog, the largest frog in North America, measuring 4 to 6 inches from end to end.

BULLFROG
Rana catesbeiana

Of all the funny things that live, in
woodland, marsh, or bog,
That creep the ground or fly the air, the
funniest thing's the frog.
The Scientific Frog (1860's)

Because the bullfrog is abundant and widely distributed, and lives well in captivity, it is one of the animals frequently used for laboratory study and experiment. The natural range of this frog is the eastern half of the United States, and in addition it has been introduced into various waterways in parts of the West, including an area of the trans-Pecos in Texas.

The bullfrog, sometimes referred to as the "jug-o-rum," is a flat, greenish, and broad-bodied creature with a large head and large eyes. The skin has remarkably few tubercles, little knobs, and there is no fold of skin along each side—a feature that differentiates it from its close relative the green frog (*R. clamitans*). The short forelegs are greenish and sometimes barred with a darker shading. The hind legs are long, muscular, and equipped with feet whose toes are long and well webbed. The underside is usually a dirty white. The male can be told from the female because the ear opening, the tympanum, behind each eye is larger than the eye itself, whereas in the female the two structures are about equal in size.

The deep boom, the "jug-o-rum," of this frog is strictly a male prerogative; it occurs in the evening and throughout the night during the warmest summer weather. To produce the booming sound, the male slowly inflates its internal vocal sac. It keeps the mouth and nostrils closed tightly, squeezing the air back and forth between the lungs and the mouth. This movement of the air forces some through slits in the floor of the mouth and into the air sac. It is then dilated into a balloonlike resonating organ which produces sounds that can be heard half a mile.

The female does not make nearly so much noise as the male. She is likely to utter a piercing squeak when injured or frightened. This is made with the mouth wide open. Both sexes emit what has been described as a loud "yarp" as they leap into the water after being startled.

The bullfrog is one of the first amphibians to hibernate and one of the last to put in an appearance in the spring. Its retirement and emergence are governed by the whereabouts of the frog on its range. Usually the bullfrog appears in the quiet parts of ponds around the middle of May, but in Texas mild weather often induces it to come out as early as February. But no matter the time of its appearance, it is soon ready to mate. This act takes place when the temperature of the air is about 80° F. and that of the water 70° F. The courting interlude of the male may last until July.

Shortly after mating, the female deposits sheets of jellylike eggs upon the surface of a stagnant pool. The egg-laying takes place from February to June because there is so much variation in climatic conditions throughout the extensive range. The number of small eggs in a mass may be ten, twenty, or twenty-five thousand, and the mass itself often covers as much as five square feet.

In areas where evaporation is great, numberless eggs never hatch. But under ordinary circumstances they hatch within four days to three weeks, depending upon daily temperatures. The larval or tadpole stage lasts two or more years, and the bullfrog-to-be may grow to a length of 3 inches. It is a greenish-gold creature with a light-colored belly, and it is sprinkled by fine yellow dots and others that are round and black. It has a flattened tail, no limbs, and a set of gills.

During its life as a tadpole, it undergoes a remarkable series of changes—a prolonged metamorphosis that transforms it from a tailed, fishlike creature to a four-legged animal without a tail and with lungs, and one that may live as long as sixteen years.

Many a tadpole never lives to undergo metamorphosis, for predators are numerous. Various fishes, many water birds, other frogs, and water snakes all include tadpoles in their diets. One of the tadpole's worst enemies is the giant water bug—a brown, flat-bodied insect with forelegs adapted for grasping. It swims alongside a tadpole, nabs it with hooklike forelegs and then sucks its body juices.

The list of predators does not decrease after the tadpole becomes a frog. It is preyed upon by such mammals as the opossum, the raccoon, and the skunk, as well as by birds and snakes. With such a host of predators, only a few young frogs become truly adult.

As a tadpole, the bullfrog feeds on algae and decaying vegetation. In its juvenile frog stage, it eats water insects and their larvae and other small, living animals. As an adult, it preys on fish and crayfish, salamanders, and mice, among other small creatures.

The bullfrog's only defense is escape. Sometimes a quick leap from bank, boulder, or other lookout into the water means safety. Once in the water it closes its nostrils and sinks to the bottom, where it is safe among the roots of pond lilies or other aquatic plants. It can stay under water for a considerable time because it absorbs oxygen from the water through its skin.

By leaping and submerging to the accompaniment of a squawk, the bullfrog often escapes its other great predator, man, who hunts this amphibian because its legs are considered a great delicacy. The bullfrog is usually sought on a dark, warm night by a hunter carrying a gig or a .22 caliber rifle, and a flash or other light. The frog's presence is betrayed when its large, bulging eyes show a bright orange-red in the light's beam. Usually there is a moment of utter immobility before the frog tries to leap to safety. In this moment the hunter frequently bags his quarry—sometimes referred to as the giant bullfrog, the jumbo, or the mammoth jumbo.

GREEN FROG
Rana clamitans

The call of the male green frog is thought to have two functions: to warn other males away from a territory and to attract females. And the voice of this close relative of the bullfrog is of sufficient volume to have earned it the name "screaming frog" on some parts of its range—a range that extends from Canada to the Gulf of Mexico and as far west as the edge of the Great Plains. Throughout this region, it frequents shallow fresh water of any kind.

The period during which the green frog breeds is April to August, depending upon its location on its range. The female expels a mass of black-and-white eggs on the surface of the water. The mass numbers as many as four thousand eggs and covers one square foot. At hatching time a tadpole measures about 2 inches from one end to the other. The transformation from tadpole to frog takes place during the second summer, between April and September.

A full-grown green frog generally measures 2 ½ inches from end to end, though there are specimens on record that attained lengths of 4 inches. The head and back of this frog may be all green or greenish brown. The sides are spotted with brown or gray, and the belly is creamy white. The adult male has a bright yellow throat. On each side there is a fold of skin—a feature lacking in the bullfrog.

The green frog feeds on some vegetation and aquatic insects and their larvae. In turn it is preyed upon by a number of animals, including hawks and crows. It is also used as bait by bass fishermen, and many are collected when partly grown for experimental work in laboratories and classrooms.

In addition to its accepted common name, green frog, and the one that comes from its voice, screaming frog, this species has at least three other popular names: spring frog, pond frog, and bronze frog. But no matter what the name, its behavior is always the same at the approach of autumn. It settles down on stream or pond bottom, buried in the mud or wedged between stones. It assumes a sprawling position, with its head slightly bent and its legs thrown out. It stays thus until late March, when the temperature of the water is about 50° F. If the temperature is much higher, the green frog is rarely dormant.

Once L. J. Cole tested the effect of temperature on the green frog's response to light. He placed several of these frogs in a black-lined box. At one end was a small hole to admit light; at the other end was a larger hole for the same purpose. If the temperature exceeded 50° F., the frogs moved toward the end with the larger opening. But when the temperature was lowered to 50° F. or less, they moved toward the darker end. This behavior was similar to their behavior during hibernation in natural surroundings.

LEOPARD FROG
Rana pipiens

The leopard frog is an amphibian of many aliases. It is known as the grass, meadow, shad, or spotted green frog, as well as the "herring hopper." Slender of body, pointed of head, the leopard frog owes this variety of names to its wide distribution. You will find it along waterways and in marshy areas from southern Canada, where it ranges from Labrador to Mackenzie, then south throughout the United States to Georgia and west to the states along the Pacific coast. There is an extension of this range in the West that runs south to Panama.

Throughout this range there is some variation in the livery of the leopard frog. In its most common form, it is a brown or green-brown frog, distinguished by two or three rows of rounded spots circled by light borders. The sides are also spotted, and there is a light line on the upper jaw. The legs are usually a vivid green, and the underside is a pure white.

In the vicinity of Massachusetts and elsewhere on the northern part of its range, the leopard frog is ready to hibernate early in October. Usually it burrows into the soft mud on the bottom of its territorial water. Sometimes one noses its way under stones, where it settles, sprawled out until spring signals that winter is over.

The leopard frog in the Massachusetts area comes out of hibernation as early as April Fool's Day, having been preceded by a few adventuresome spring peepers and some of the wood frogs. The male is thought to signal for a mate by emitting a grunting sort of croak. Shortly after mating the female discharges her eggs in masses of flattened clumps in the water in which she mated. A tadpole that hatches early in the season, changes into frog form by July or August. It promptly leaves the water for any nearby marsh. By the time one is fully grown, it measures 2 to 3½ inches, perhaps as much as 4 inches in an unusually large specimen.

The variation among leopard frogs is such that they have been classified as northern, southern, Rio Grande, Vegas valley, and western. And in parts of Minnesota and neighboring states, some of these frogs lack spots and others have a much darker skin. These mutants are occasionally classified as subspecies and given the scientific names *R. p. burnsi* and *R. p. kandiyohi.*

PICKEREL FROG
Rana palustris

The pickerel frog is frequently mistaken for the leopard frog —a species that has a slight edge on it as to size. The pickerel frog is smaller—2 or 3 inches in length—and dotted with squarish spots outlined in a darker shade. There are similar spots on the sides of this yellowish-brown species, whose hind legs are bright orange on the inside. The body is slender, the head short, and the nose or snout rounded.

The pickerel frog is much more inclined to stay near water than is the leopard frog. It frequents bogs, marshes, ponds, and cold streams on a range that extends from Canada's Maritime Provinces to the Carolinas in the eastern United States, then west as far as eastern prairie country, and south into parts of Texas.

Early in May the female discharges clusters of globular eggs in masses numbering two or three thousand. She attaches these to submerged twigs or to the underwater parts of aquatic plants. The pickerel frog-to-be hatches as a minute creature, with a lustrous skin and legs that lack color on the undersides. At the end of a seventy-day interval the tadpole becomes a frog, measuring about 1½ inches from end to end. Now it starts to feed on such meadow insects as grasshoppers and crickets, beetles, flies, and millers, as well as crayfish and worms.

Among the many colloquial names of this member of the Ranidae is that of poison frog. This is because it secretes a fluid that irritates the mouth of any predator seizing it. Such frog-eating reptiles as the garter, the water, and the ribbon snake leave the pickerel frog alone. Though the secretion is reported to kill such other frogs as the spring peeper, the wood and the green frogs, the bullfrog eats the pickerel frog without any evident distress.

This frog, so called because it makes excellent bait for pickerel, is a wanderer. It often leaves the vicinity of the water to visit nearby fields, weedy patches, and even the entrances of caves. Because it is numerous and addicted to this habit, it is easily caught by fishermen and other frog hunters.

The croaking of the pickerel frog has been described in a number of ways. The author of *The Frog Book*, Mary C. Dickerson, says it is "like the sound produced by tearing a resisting cloth of some sort." Roger Conant describes it as "a steady, low-pitched snore of one or two seconds' duration but with little carrying power." The male is the one that does this "singing," with the aid of two vocal pouches. Some singing or calling is accomplished while a male is under water.

The pickerel frog is a late hibernator; it may not settle down for the winter until the end of September or even until October. The interval of hibernation is often passed on the bottom of a stream where some water flows all winter long. A warm winter day rouses one of these frogs sufficiently so that it crawls around on the stream bottom. However, the pickerel frog does not come out of hibernation until the water temperature is 45° F. or higher. On the northern part of its range, this means the pickerel frog puts in its first appearance of the year toward the middle of April.

WOOD FROG
Rana sylvatica

The call of the fawn-colored wood frog is often heard before the ice has gone out of the ponds and lakes on a range that extends farther north than that of any other amphibian or reptile in North America. Its quacklike call is heard in moist woodland country from Labrador to Alaska, on the most northerly parts of its range, and in like habitats throughout the eastern United States as far south as central Georgia. To the west the distribution is uneven, with populations in the Ozark Mountains and in parts of Kansas, Colorado, Wyoming, and Idaho.

The wood frog breeds in shallow water, including the tundra ponds of the Far North. In some areas the female discharges her eggs as early as March. As soon as the mating is consummated and the eggs are discharged, the adults quit their respective pools and make for nearby woods and forests. Now the males are silent creatures and will remain so until the next breeding season. By midsummer the tadpole has transformed into a tiny brown frog resembling the adult.

The overall measurement of an adult wood frog varies from 1⅜ inches to as much as 3¼ inches, with the average length somewhere between these two. The usual color is fawn, though some individuals are a decided pinkish-brown. There is a dark patch or mask that extends backward from the eyes. Along each side is a yellow stripe that separates the color on the upper side from the dirty-white of the underside. This livery encases a slender-bodied frog with a small, pointed head.

Other North American species in the family Ranidae (the "true frogs") include the mink frog (*R. septentrionalis*). It is a small frog of New England and New York and of country as far west as Minnesota. It is also found in Canada as far north as Hudson Bay. This species, light olive spotted with brown, is so named because it gives off the odor of a mink when handled.

One of the best spots to look for this small frog is a pond or lake in which there are plenty of water lilies. It uses the pads as stepping stones, jumping from one to another. The mink frog, like all the small Ranidae, is an excellent leaper, though neither it nor its allies are in a class with the agile frog (*R. dalmatina*) of Europe. This species has executed a long-jump record of seven feet.

Another of the true frogs is the gopher (*R. capito*), whose subspecific forms are the dusky gopher frog and the Florida gopher frog. The dusky form, a warty frog, is found in the coastal plain of the Carolinas and as far south as east-central Georgia. The Florida gopher frog is generally light in color, sometimes so light that it is nearly white. It calls in a deep roar along the coastal plain from Georgia to southern Florida.

Two of our most colorful true frogs are indigenous to the Far West. One is the red-legged frog (*R. aurora*), whose specific name suggests how striking its color is. One form of this frog is found in California, and the name of another (*R. a. cascadae*) gives a clue as to its whereabouts. The second of these gaily colored frogs is *R. boylei*, a yellow-legged creature measuring 2 inches in length and well covered with warts. It is native to California as are the subspecies, the San Bernardino yellow-legged frog (*R. b. muscosa*) and the Sierra yellow-legged frog (*R. b. sierrae*).

These are representatives of the true frogs, the Ranidae, in North America. They are thought of as being typical frogs because they are usually long-legged species with narrow waists and smooth skins. The family has worldwide distribution and includes several genera, of which *Rana* is far the largest.

TREE FROGS or "TOADS"
Hyla

"With many frogs and toads the colours evidently
serve as a protection, such as the bright green
tints of the tree frogs . . ."
CHARLES DARWIN, *Origin of Species*

Olympic National Park of Washington is a piece of original
America. It is a living wilderness of more than 888,000 acres and
unique because climatic conditions make it a temperate-zone rain
forest. Among the wild creatures of this area is the Pacific tree
frog or "toad" (*Hyla regilia*), one North American representative of a family that has worldwide distribution.

The members of the family to which the Pacific tree frog belongs are usually distinguished by slim waists, long legs, and toes
that end in adhesive disks or pads. Most of these tiny frogs undergo
pronounced color changes—changes influenced by activity, light,
moisture, and temperature. And they are creatures of many habitats: a few are arboreal; others shelter in low, brushy thickets; a
great many frequent swamps and moist woodlands; and still others
live on the ground or burrow in it.

The tree frogs, often heard but seldom seen, are frequently referred to as hylas. Perhaps the best-known hyla in North America
is the spring peeper (*H. crucifer*), found from the Maritime
Provinces of Canada, as far south in the East as northern Florida,
and westward in the North to eastern Manitoba and in the South
as far as eastern Texas.

The spring peeper reaches an overall length of ¾ inch to 1¼
inches. It may be gray, light brown, or olive. There is a mark
on its back that is roughly in the form of an X. It is rarely perfect
in outline, but is still distinguishable as a cross, and is the reason
for the specific name *crucifer*, Latin for "cross-bearing." It does
not undergo the color changes common to many of its close relatives.

H. crucifer wakes early from hibernation, roused by the barest

hint of warmth. In fact this little frog is so sensitive to any indication of warm-weather-to-come that it has been heard peeping on
Long Island as early as January, when the temperature was 58° F.
A more usual time for an appearance is mid-March. At first there
is only an occasional "pe-ep, pe-ep, pe-ep, pe-ep." But when a
pond is full of wide-awake peepers, the combined calls sound like
distantly heard pipes played in a treble key. The chorus is so
high-pitched, acute, and shrill that it has an eerie quality—one that
evokes the impression of a time early in the world's evolution.

The voice of the early-out spring peeper is often stilled by a
cold wave. But this interval is never long-lasting, for if you have
heard this frog, you know that as soon as the weather warms once
more you will hear it again.

The male arrives first at the breeding pond, where the calling
takes place. He overwintered on land, under an accumulation
of leaves or other natural litter. The female gets to the pond somewhat later. Both sexes are usually in the pond by mid-April and
often stay there until the end of May.

Shortly after mating the female releases her eggs one at a time.
She spends a day or so discharging the eight to twelve hundred
fertilized eggs. Most are attached to the underwater parts of plants,
but some wash back and forth on the bottom. An egg hatches in
five to fifteen days, and the future peeper emerges as a tadpole
about one inch long. It remains in this stage for some ninety days,
growing another half inch. Then during July it transforms into
a frog measuring half an inch or slightly less. Now it leaves the
water to join the other young frogs and adults for life on land.
Before it reaches the breeding stage, it will be three or four years
old. The behavior of the spring peeper in the South differs from
that of one in the North, for the southern form is a winter frog
that breeds from November to March.

The spring peeper is silent during the latter half of the summer.
It passes most of its time on the ground hunting for a wide variety
of tiny insects and is, according to E. Laurence Palmer, "essentially
useful as a check on insects." It also eats an occasional small snail
or earthworm. The rest of the time it perches in low, shrubby
growths, where it is so inconspicuous that it is rarely seen. And

from time to time it climbs high in a tree, aided by the disks on its feet.

The best time to locate a spring peeper is at night and during the interval while it is calling. It is likely to be clinging to a reed, floating on a drifting twig, or sitting on the leaf of the umbrella-like May apple. The call acts as a "locator." And a flashlight is a "spot" that makes it possible to see *Hyla crucifer* in the act of peeping. It assumes a singing stance by rearing back on its haunches. So poised, it inflates its tiny white throat until it looks like a shiny bubble. Now, with its mouth closed, it pipes, "Pe-ep, pe-ep, pe-ep, pe-ep . . ." until the air supply is exhausted and the throat is deflated. Now there is a bag of loose skin under the throat. And it seems impossible that this tiny creature is capable of a call with so much volume that it may be heard for a mile.

GREEN TREE FROG
Hyla cinerea

This bright green species frequents a coastal range from the Delmarva Peninsula to the Florida Keys; it is also found west from Florida along the Gulf coast to central Texas, and northward as far as southern Illinois. Throughout this range it is known by such regional names as cinereous frog, because at times it is an ashy gray, the Carolina tree frog, the fried-bacon frog, the bell frog, and the cowbell frog. The last two names are singularly appropriate because the call has a ringing quality that is often heard as many as seventy-five times a minute.

In the South this breeding call rings out from March to October, but on the northerly parts of the range it is heard in the spring. At the breeding season the males collect in what are known as congresses. These gatherings often number many hundreds of calling green tree-frogs. The sound that results is rather like a series of off-key cowbells all being rung at once.

The green tree frog requires about two months to change from a tadpole into its adult form. As a tadpole, it is a bright green little creature with yellowish stripes on the sides of the head. As an adult, it is a smooth-skinned animal with exceedingly long legs and a somewhat pointed head. The eyes are large and prominent. The usual overall length is 1¼ to 2¼ inches.

Though this frog is usually pictured as bright green, it undergoes color changes that turn it to ashy gray, yellow-green, or dark green. And it is usually brown when calling at night. The underside—known, too, as the venter—is white or yellow-white. There is generally a white or yellow stripe along each side that widens near the ears.

The green tree frog is more aquatic than some of the other hylas. It frequents such moist places as the swampy edges of ponds, streams, and brooks. It spends much of its time adhering to tall aquatic plants and to the vegetation lining the shores. During its active season this frog sloughs its skin every evening.

GRAY OR COMMON TREE FROG
Hyla versicolor

Frequently this frog is spoken of as a tree toad. And there is some reason for this misnomer because it has a somewhat rough and warty skin. Its basic color varies; it may be ashy gray, nearly white, pale brown, or a washed-out green. The mark on its upper side is star-shaped, and the inside of each hind leg is a bright orange. It is the largest tree frog in the North, measuring at full growth 1¼ to 2 inches in overall length.

Its range is eastern North America from New Brunswick, Canada, to northern Florida, and then as far west as Kansas. On the northern parts of its range, the gray tree frog begins to disappear in late summer. It settles down for hibernation in hollows between the roots of trees or at the bottom of a cavity in a tree trunk or partially rotted stump. In Georgia and presumably on other parts of its southern range, it does not hibernate until November.

The spring reappearance is generally late in April, though it varies throughout the range. The males and the females breed in shallow water from April to August. The female is likely to discharge her eggs around the first of June; then she leaves at once for the land area that is her home range. An egg hatches in about five days, and the tadpole that emerges is greenish-gold with a red tail.

During this stage it is preyed on by diving beetles, fish, and small water snakes.

The tadpole stage lasts about seven weeks. The next stage in the life of this frog begins when it emerges from the water. Now it is about ½ inch in length, and now it is a land creature except for the seasonal breeding interval. It spends much of its time either motionless on a twig or branch, or searching for tiny insects in the crevices of bark, in stumps of dead trees, and in other likely places. Sometimes it leaps into the air to capture prey on the wing. During its land life it is usually a silent creature, but as soon as the mating season arrives, it starts to call. This is a short, loud trilling that lasts from one to three seconds.

The largest of our tree frogs is an exotic. It is the Cuban tree frog (*H. septentrionalis*), native to Cuba and the Bahamas but now established on the Florida Keys and in the southeastern part of this state. A greenish or bronze species, it comes in two sizes: the male has an overall measurement of 1½ to 3½ inches, whereas the female is 2 to 5 inches long. It hunts by night for insects, snails, and other frogs.

There is one tropical species in the United States. This is the Mexican tree frog (*H. baudini*), a species that undergoes marked color changes. Sometimes it is a pale yellow or gray and sometimes it is a dark gray or green. Its range is from the lower Rio Grande Valley as far south as Honduras. During dry weather it shelters in the damp cavities of trees, or under natural litter, or else burrows into the ground. The Mexican tree frog could well be one described by Aesop in his fable, "The Frogs' Complaint Against The Sun":

Once upon a time, when the Sun announced his intention to take a wife, the Frogs lifted up their voices in a clamor to the sky. Jupiter, disturbed by the noise of their croaking, inquired the cause of their complaint. One of them said, "The Sun, now while he is single, parches up the marsh, and compels us to die miserably in our arid homes; what will be our future condition if he should beget other suns?"

Two North American tree frogs of differing species sometimes mate to produce a hybrid whose call is intermediate between those of the parents. One of these is the barking tree frog (*H. gratiosa*) of the coastal plain from the Carolinas to southern Florida. This species, so named for its barking call, is known to mate with the green tree frog (*H. cinerea*). The resultant offspring is likely to be intermediate in size between the parents, but looks much more like the green frog than the barking species.

The call of this hybrid as recorded by the sound spectrogram has a dominant frequency of some 900 cycles. The call of *gratiosa* registered a dominant frequency of 600 cycles, while that of *cinerea* was 1,200 cycles. A hybrid such as this often calls with a chorus composed of all barking frogs.

The smallest tree frog is also one of the tiniest in North America. The species so distinguished is the little grass frog (*H. ocularis*), measuring $\frac{7}{16}$ to $\frac{5}{8}$ inch. It calls on a range that starts in southeastern Virginia and extends to the tip of Florida.

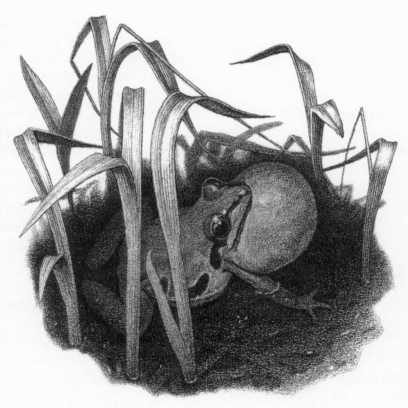

Ornate Chorus Frog, *Pseudacris ornata*

CHORUS FROGS
Pseudacris

The chorus frogs belong to a genus found only in North America. These tiny frogs are characterized by slender bodies, pointed snouts, and slightly webbed toes. And they are not climbers to any extent, for their toe disks are small.

Among the dozen or so species and subspecies of these indigenous North America frogs is one distinguished by a black mask. This is the ornate chorus frog (*Pseudacris ornata*), a creature that is something of a quick-change artist when it comes to color. At one moment this tiny frog is almost black, but shortly thereafter it may transform into a nearly white frog. At other times it is green with pronounced red spots. Its most usual color is russet dotted with black patches along each side, and with the inside of each leg peppered with pin-point dots of yellow.

The ornate chorus frog frequents a range that includes the coastal plain from North Carolina to eastern Louisiana and on south throughout most of Florida. It is found in wet and water areas that dot pine barrens and stands of cypress, as well as in extremely watery meadows. In such areas it sounds off with a shrill peep during late fall, winter, and early spring. The calling is done by the male, who has a single, round vocal pouch.

The species of chorus frog known scientifically as *P. nigrita* is represented by a number of races or forms. One of these is the western chorus frog—known, too, as the striped chorus frog and the three-striped chorus frog. As a rule this frog has three dark stripes down its gray, brown, or olive back. The underside is almost white. Some individuals have the throat and chest dotted with dark spots, but all individuals are distinguished by a light line along the upper lip. Though the toes are equipped with adhesive disks, this species climbs no higher than the branches of low bushes.

The western, striped, or three-striped chorus frog breeds in ditches, swamps, or temporary water on a range that starts in southern Quebec and western New York and extends as far west as Kansas and Oklahoma. Its mating call sounds like "reap, reap, reap," with each *p* accented by a rising inflection. On the southern part of its range the call is heard as early as February, but farther north it may not be heard until June.

The female attaches small egg masses to the leaves and stems of plants growing in water. The tadpoles or polliwogs that hatch are tiny and transform during June, if they happen to be in Missouri. One of these frogs does not "grow up" to be large, for its average length is ¾ inch to 1½ inches—lengths shorter than the measurement of its full scientific name, *Pseudacris nigrita triseriata*.

Another of the frogs in this genus is the boreal chorus frog (*P. n. septentrionalis*), a short-legged form whose range extends farther north than that of any of its relatives. This brown or greenish frog is found from Great Bear Lake in northwestern Canada south into Colorado and Utah. Because its legs are so short in comparison with those of other frogs, it hops rather than leaps over the marshy areas it frequents. Its call is similar to that of the western chorus frog, a "reap, reap, reap." with each *p* stressed by a rising inflection.

CRICKET FROG
Acris gryllus

The call of the cricket frog is a fast-paced "gick, gick, gick." This similarity to the stridulation of the common cricket is the reason for this frog's popular name. Depending upon the latitude, the cricket frog calls from February until the end of October on a range that includes most of the territory east of the Rocky Mountains from Canada to the Gulf of Mexico.

Throughout this range, this non-climbing member of the tree frog family frequents shallow water that affords cover—emergent aquatic plants or the types of plants growing along the shore. And the setting must be open enough to let in plenty of sunlight.

The female who responds to a mating call lays her eggs sometime between April or May and the beginning of August. Her eggs are few in number; they are expelled one at a time, and are attached to plants in the pond or pool in which she mated. The tadpole that hatches is longer than the body of the parent, but at the end of six or eight weeks it transforms into a frog measuring no more than half an inch.

As an adult the cricket frog is a warty little creature, with an overall measurement of an inch or an inch and a half. Its basic color is gray, green, or brown marked with dots and splotches of red, orange, yellow, or black. There is a dark V between the eyes, and there are stripes or spots on each thigh. The male is equipped with a single vocal pouch under the throat.

The cricket frog is a lively species, getting about by a series of erratic leaps. This liveliness seems to carry over into winter, for it is active or semiactive in the milder climates of its range during this season. Only during the coldest weather does it become truly dormant, secreting itself beneath piles of leaves or crawling between rocks. But if the weather moderates, it pops out for an active interlude.

OTHER, LESS FAMILIAR FROGS

One of North America's less familiar frogs is the robber or barking frog (*Eleutherodactylus latrans*) of central Texas and southeastern New Mexico. It lives in caves and limestone ledges, where it climbs about easily because it can hold on with its long fingers. Its call is similar to that of a distantly heard barking dog. In late winter or early spring the female deposits her eggs in rain-filled crevices. The tadpoles do not hatch, but remain in the eggs and undergo the transformation from tadpoles to frogs before they emerge.

Tadpole-less frogs are not an oddity in the rain-forest canopy of Cuba. Here, some frogs lay their eggs in pools formed in the hollows of large leaves. The tadpoles hatch as frogs, the metamorphosis having been completed within the egg. Such frogs are found only in the tops of tall trees in the mountains. One spot in Cuba for collecting tadpole-less frogs is the summit of Pico Turquino in the Sierra Maestro Mountains.

An immigrant from Cuba has become established in Florida. This is the greenhouse frog (*Eleutherodactylus ricordi planirostris*), a tiny brown species that lays its eggs on land in damp places. The development takes place within the egg, and at hatching the minute frog has a snippet of a tail.

The lower Rio Grande Valley is the northernmost part of the range of the Mexican white-lipped frog (*Leptodactylus labialis*), a smooth-skinned species that is categorized as a nest-building frog. It lays eggs in a frothy mass and when they hatch, the full-fledged frogs appear.

And finally there are the two chirping or whistling frogs. One is the Rio Grande frog (*Syrrhophus campi*), a gray, brown, or olive species of southernmost Texas. The other whistling or chirping frog is found from central Texas to Big Bend country. Its common name is cliff frog and its scientific name is *S. marnocki*. This species in encased in a smooth green skin dotted with brown. It is slightly larger than the Rio Grande frog (⅝ to 1 inch), for it measures ¾ inch to 1½ inches. Both these frogs have a chirping, birdlike call.

These less familiar species complete this section on North American frogs—animals that cannot always be clearly distinguished from toads—usually less streamlined than frogs and much slower-moving animals.

AMERICAN TOAD
Bufo terrestris americanus

"The toad, without which no garden would be complete."
CHARLES DUDLEY WARNER

Early in the spring the American toad comes out of hibernation, During the winter months it has lain dormant, buried about three feet deep in loose soil. Sometimes the overwintering spot is close to the foundation of a house or some other heated building. Such a spot provides a little extra security against winter because it affords some slight warmth. The first to dig to the surface is usually the male, one in its third or fourth year. Such a toad starts for the nearest shallow breeding pond, with its departure timed for early evening.

The male, distinguished by an almost black throat, hops along through the night until he reaches his destination. As soon as he is in the water, he begins a prolonged trilling. The call, sustained, sweet, and somewhat tremulous, is heard day and night. Throughout the Middle Atlantic states the trilling is a part of the natural music that marks the end of April and the beginning of May.

Early in the season only a few males call, but as more and more come out of hibernation and make their way to the water, the number calling increases until the trilling chorus is almost constant. The singing males are soon joined by the younger males and the females. Now both sexes paddle around in the water to the accompaniment of the males' trilling, which increases in tempo on rainy days.

The swimming interlude in a female's life comes to an end when she lays her jellylike strings of eggs, black and white and measuring $\frac{1}{12}$ inch in length. A string often reaches a length of 70 feet, and the number of eggs in the strings varies from four to twelve thousand. They are expelled just beneath the surface, but as the days go by they sink to the bottom.

The tiny eggs hatch within three to ten days, depending upon air and water temperatures. The toads-to-be are black during the tadpole stage, which lasts forty to sixty days. Now the shallowest parts of the pond or pool are full of polliwogs—easy prey for birds, fishes, turtles, and the larvae of certain water insects. The tadpoles that survive transform into tiny toads, measuring $\frac{2}{5}$ inch in length. Now they are ready to come ashore, where they stay in the vicinity of the water for ten to fourteen days. During this interval many are preyed upon by snakes and by some of the predators of their tadpole days.

This waiting interval close to the water is a time during which all the toad characteristics are fully developed. Now the young toads scatter, each making its way to its own home range. This movement accelerates during damp or rainy weather. As a young toad grows, it sheds its skin every few weeks. An older toad also gets a new livery three or four times during its active season. The skin splits and as it works loose, the toad pulls it into its mouth and swallows it.

The American toad matures in two or three years. The male is always smaller than the female, rarely exceeding a length of 3½ inches, whereas the overall length of the female is as much as 5½ inches. Most full-grown American toads are a plain brown, though some individuals have a gray, olive, or reddish cast to the skin. The spots are black or brown, with one or two good-sized warts in each of the larger dark spots. The color of the warts is red, dark brown, yellow, or orange. There are two large glands, the parotoids back of the prominent eyes. The underside has a scattering of dark spots.

The range of the American toad, known also as the hoptoad, is extensive. It is found from the area of Hudson's Bay south throughout the eastern half of the United States as far as Maryland. South of this state it frequents elevations of five thousand feet in various mountain areas. Other species and subspecies extend the range west to the Pacific coast and south into Mexico.

The variety of habitats in which you find this toad is great. Whether the territory is mountain-high or valley-low, it must offer shallow water for breeding, plenty of shelter and moisture, and an abundant supply of food—especially insects, of which many are crop and garden pests. Under normal circumstances the toad fills and empties its stomach several times during a night's hunting.

After spending the day secreted in a moist, sheltered spot, the hoptoad begins to hunt in the early evening and continues to forage throughout most of the night. As it hops over its territory in search of prey, it is frequently the victim of such other night-hunting animals as hawks and owls, as well as of snakes and skunks.

The toad hunts for ants, chinch bugs, cutworms, potato beetles, and earthworms—to name but a few of the many creatures in its diet. Once it spots an insect, the toad closes in with a series of cautious hops. This approach can be likened to a cat stalking a mouse, for it is wary, deliberate, and a prelude to death. When it is within striking distance, the predator halts, then cocks its head first to one side and then to the other, sighting for a kill. Suddenly the toad flicks out its 2-inch, sticky tongue, which is attached to the front of the mouth. It manages its tongue so adroitly that it rarely misses a target. The victim adheres to the tongue and is thrown back into the mouth. The tongue action of a hunting toad is so rapid that it is almost impossible to follow.

The consumption of insects by the American toad during its active season amounts to thousands. In *Hand Book for the Curious,* a 1936 publication, Paul Griswold Howes writes, "From a single not overlarge toad taken in the morning after his night of hunting, I removed twenty-two large carpenter ants, two large-sized moth larvae, two sow bugs, five weevils, one flower beetle, one cricket, ten red ants, and five grasshoppers." From this evidence it is easy to understand why the toad is rated as having an annual value of about twenty dollars to gardeners and agriculturists.

The French think so highly of the toad as a natural control of insects that they buy this amphibian for release in gardens—well aware that, after the initial cost, they have a long-lived destroyer of pests and one that does not disturb the balance of nature as is so often true in the use of man-made controls. In China the toad serves man in a passive role; its skin contains adrenalin and is used as a medicine to increase lowered blood pressure.

During its active season the toad sometimes relies on its only means of self-defense. This is a white, acrid fluid secreted by the parotoid glands during moments of danger or great pain. A dog that attacks a hoptoad rarely bothers one a second time, for this fluid irritates the eyes and the mouth—something to recall in handling a toad. (The secretion of the giant toad (*B. marinus*) can cause blindness to a man or a dog.)

The hoptoad secretes another fluid when handled. This is watery, colorless, and harmless, and does not cause warts, as many people believe. A skunk that has caught a toad is said to rub its catch over the ground to remove this secretion.

As the toad's active season wanes, it ceases feeding. It spends this prehibernation interval either hopping about restlessly or sitting in some protected spot. On the northern parts of its range, it goes into hibernation as soon as cool September weather sets in. It burrows into loose soil, working its way into the ground in a backward position. It uses its long hind legs to throw the earth to each side, and at the same time it pushes itself in with its short front legs. One often digs and pushes until it is three or four feet beneath the surface. Then it settles down in the hibernating chamber with the head bent between the front feet and the hind feet drawn as close to the body as possible. It stays in this position until the following spring when the air temperature is 48° to 50° F. This means that the toads in the Middle Atlantic and New England states emerge any time from late March until the end of April.

The emerging toads vary in color. On the northernmost parts of the range, in the vicinity of Hudson Bay, they are brightly colored. The toad coming out of hibernation in the mountainous parts of New Hampshire is sometimes almost a Venetian red, whereas the Cape Cod species is likely to be as pale as the sands from which it crawls.

OTHER TRUE TOADS
Bufonidae

Another of the true toads (*Bufo*) is Fowler's, known scientifically as *B. woodhousei fowleri*. This 2-to-3-inch toad is found on a range that starts in central New England and extends south and southwest into Texas and in the North west as far as Michigan. It is particularly common in Massachusetts and the states to the south.

Fowler's toad goes into hibernation earlier than the American toad and also emerges later in the spring. It sometimes overwinters by itself, or it may hibernate as one of a group that settles down in an oval chamber 9 to 12 inches below the earth's surface. As soon as the male shakes off his winter lethargy, he works his way to the surface, then hops off to the nearest shallow water—an irrigation ditch, the margin of a lake or pond, or even a temporary pool. Here it starts to call—a call short, nasal, and decidedly unmusical. The call has been described as a pronounced "waah" or "wauk," with the latter sound consisting of two syllables, a *wau* and then a lowered *k*. Breeding occurs from late spring until the

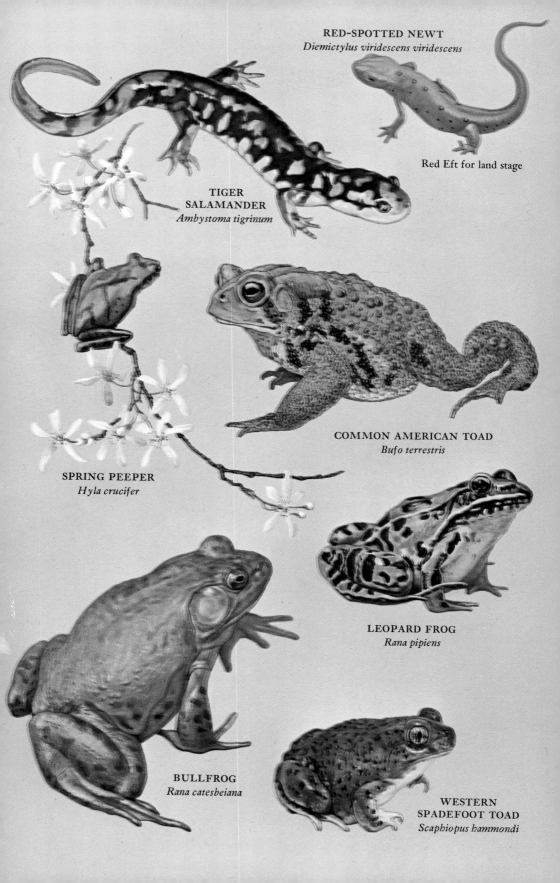

RED-SPOTTED NEWT
Diemictylus viridescens viridescens

Red Eft for land stage

TIGER SALAMANDER
Ambystoma tigrinum

COMMON AMERICAN TOAD
Bufo terrestris

SPRING PEEPER
Hyla crucifer

LEOPARD FROG
Rana pipiens

BULLFROG
Rana catesbeiana

WESTERN SPADEFOOT TOAD
Scaphiopus hammondi

middle of August. The female lays two strings of eggs, leaving them to hatch unattended as she returns to the land, where she remains until the next breeding season. This toad is named for S. P. Fowler, who was one of Massachusett's first naturalists.

The subspecific relatives of Fowler's toad include the Rocky Mountain toad (*B. w. woodhousei*), whose low-pitched call is heard from the Dakotas and western Missouri all the way to southeastern Washington and then on south into Mexico. This species, reported to have a nondescript appearance, is common in Cub Lake Valley, Hallowell Park, and the Ouzel Lake area in the Wild Basin of Rocky Mountain National Park. Late in the spring Rocky Mountain toads gather in large numbers in the waters of these areas. The females lay strings of eggs which hatch small tadpoles. By the end of the summer the tadpoles transform into frogs and repair to the land.

Another of the subspecific relatives of Fowler's toad is the East Texas toad (*B. w. velatus*), a dark-breasted amphibian of northeastern Texas. The Dakota toad (*B. w. hemiophrys*) and the southwestern Woodhouse's toad (*B. w. australis*) complete the roster of toads in this particular group.

The smallest toad in North America belonging to the genus *Bufo* is the gray-black oak toad (*B. quercicus*), which frequents the coastal plain from North Carolina south and into the greater part of Florida and then inland to eastern Louisiana. This species has an overall length of ¾ inch to 1¼ inches. Its size makes it a dwarf when compared to the giant toad (*B. marinus*), which has a record measurement of 9 inches, though a more usual length is 4 to 6 inches. This behemoth *Bufo* calls on a range that starts in extreme southeastern Texas and extends all the way to Patagonia. It has been introduced in other areas, including Florida in the neighborhood of Miami.

A common species of the South is *B. terrestris*, an amphibian of the night that has been named "the charming toad" in some regions. The reason for such a cognomen is a legend extant in the Southeast, which has it that if you stare at this toad long enough your eyes will turn green.

SPADEFOOT TOADS
Scaphiopus

Fossil spadefoots, apparently little different from
present-day forms, have been found in rock beds that
were laid down more than twelve million years ago.
KENNETH L. GOSNER
Natural History, September 1957

The spadefoot toad is distinguished by large eyes with vertical
pupils and fleshy, webbed feet equipped with horny, spadelike
wedges on each hind foot. These spades vary in shape and size,
depending on the species; some are elongate and shaped like a
sickle, whereas others are short and shaped like a wedge. In addition
this toad may be identified by a skin less warty than that of other
species, and by the lack of noticeable parotoid glands behind the
ears.

Of all the spadefoots occurring in North America, only one is
found east of the Mississippi River. This is the eastern spadefoot
toad, known scientifically as *Scaphiopus holbrooki*, a dark brown
species with lengthwise stripes of yellow. The spade on the outer
edge of each hind foot is long and shaped like a sickle. And there
is no little hump, or boss, between the eyes.

The eastern spadefoot, like all its close relatives, is a great burrower. At the end of its nightly activities it digs into the ground,
where it passes the day. Since this is habitual the spadefoot is
frequently unknown even in areas where it is common on its
range—a range that extends from southern New England to southern Florida. Throughout this range, the eastern spadefoot frequents
woodsy areas where the soil is loose or even sandy.

When it is ready to hibernate, the spadefoot digs in to a depth
of 3 or 4 feet. It usually makes its overwintering burrow on a hill-
side facing south. It hibernates in a chamber barely large enough
to accommodate its body, even in a crouching position with the
legs drawn close to the body.

As soon as the female rouses in the spring, she hops to a breeding pond. Here the males are calling in a low-keyed grunt. Breeding almost always occurs during a heavy rainfall, sometimes starting as early as January and often lasting until September. The female discharges her eggs in jellylike bands during a two-day interval; two weeks to two months later, a one-inch tadpole emerges. When a tadpole transforms into a toad, it is a little animal with an overall measurement of about ½ inch. And by the time it is fully grown, it has a short, compact body measuring at its greatest length 2¼ inches. A more usual length is not quite 2 inches.

A close relative of the eastern spadefoot is distinguished by a little hump, the boss, between the eyes. This is Hurter's spadefoot (*S. hurteri*), named for Julius Hurter, a herpetologist who worked in Missouri. This toad, a greenish species, frequents a range that extends from central Arkansas and western Louisiana to a boundary that runs from central Oklahoma to central Texas.

Another toad in this group is named for Darius Nash Couch, a graduate of the United States Military Academy in the class of 1846. Couch served in the Mexican War, and for services at Buena Vista was brevetted first lieutenant in 1847. He was also a member of the United States and Mexican Boundary Survey. As an avocation he studied and collected specimens of the fauna of the arid and semiarid regions in which he served and fought. One such specimen was the spadefoot toad that now bears his name, *S. couchi*. The livery of Couch's toad has a decidedly yellowish cast, though the basic color is green. The call of *S. couchi* is not melodious, for it has a bleating quality that brings to mind the baaing of a strayed sheep. The largest known measurement of this toad is 3½ inches from one end to the other.

Other spadefoots are the plains (*S. bombifrons*) of the Great Plains and the western (*S. hammondi*) of the short-grass plains regions. These two and their close relatives are all beneficial, for the food they consume is largely insects, including many that are categorized as pests. They catch prey with a lightning-like flick of the tongue; it is attached to the front of the mouth and coated with a sticky substance that glues the victim in place for rapid transfer to the mouth.

NARROW-MOUTHED TOADS
Microhyla

The narrow-mouthed toad (*M. carolinensis*) and various sub-species form a group of tailless amphibians that are seldom seen because they are so strictly creatures of the night. The male can be differentiated from the female by a dark throat patch as opposed to the light one of the female. Both sexes are small, stout, and pointed of head. Their legs are short, so that they run rather than hop. From time to time running is interrupted by short jumps of not much more than an inch or so.

The eastern narrow-mouthed toad (*M. c. carolinensis*) frequents a range that extends from Maryland to the Florida Keys and thence west to Missouri and. Texas. It is a frog of moist areas in which there are plenty of hiding places. A home range is often the marshy edge of a stream or pond where there is a lot of natural litter, or such refuse as the tag ends of trees and boards or other waste from logging and lumbering operations. Here one of these toad shelters by day, coming out by night to hunt for such prey as ants, beetles, and termites.

The breeding season is a long one—mid-April until October. This toad breeds either in extremely shallow water or in water on which there is floating vegetation such as duckweed, spatterdock, or pond lily. A male calls from a hidden position, emitting a sort of bleating buzz. Though this is one of the least attractive among the toad calls, it seems to have sufficient appeal to lure the female to the breeding area. Eggs are laid subsequently, tadpoles hatch in due time, and frog forms develop eventually.

A full-grown eastern narrow-mouthed toad measures $\frac{7}{8}$ inch to $1\frac{1}{4}$ inches in overall length. This species is subject to some color variation: sometimes an individual is gray, then again it may be brown, or at another time its color is red. There is a dark stripe down the center of the back, and the underside is marked by numerous small dots.

The western form is the Great Plains narrow-mouthed toad, known scientifically as *M. c. olivacea*. It frequents a range that starts in Nebraska and Missouri and extends south into northern Mexico. It is a gray-green amphibian whose skin is virtually unmarked. The volume of its call is small, in keeping with the size of its body. The call sounds like the buzz of a bumble bee, and this seems exactly right for an animal measuring no more than ⅞ of an inch to 1½ inches. You can hear this buzz, sometimes preceded by a "peep," from early March until late September. It is most frequent after a period of heavy rains.

The secretive narrow-mouthed toad, the burrowing spadefoot, and the common American toad have counterparts in many parts of the world. In England, for instance, a close relative of the hoptoad is the common toad (B. bufo)—a species that occurs throughout Great Britain, though not in Ireland, and all over Europe as far east as mid-Asia. Another toad of the British Isles is the natterjack (B. calamita). This toad is described in *The British Amphibia And Reptiles*, a field study book by L. Harrison Matthews, as "running 'like a mouse' being unable to hop because of the shortness of the hind legs."

These British toads and their relatives in North America belong to the Bufonidae, a family that is nearly worldwide in distribution and that for the most part is long-lived. For some species have a life span of at least twenty and perhaps even thirty years.

SALAMANDERS
AND NEWTS

"A salamander is a kind of heroine in chastity,
that treads upon fire, and lives in the midst
of flames without being hurt."
JOSEPH ADDISON, *The Spectator*
October 17, 1771

Addison apparently subscribed to the old, old belief that the
salamander has the power to endure fire without harm. This
belief has been extant since the Middle Ages when, as in later years,
wood was gathered in the forests, brought inside, and stacked near
the hearth for future use. As the wood dried, salamanders often
crawled from beneath the bark and scampered about the room.
Thus it was natural enough to believe that this tailed amphibian
had emerged from the fire burning on the hearth. Today in Europe
one species is known as the fire salamander as a result of this belief.

The name for these odd animals comes from a Greek word meaning "fire animal"—a misnomer, for the salamander shuns heat and
is a creature that requires a great deal of moisture in order to live.
Though these "fire animals" are similar in appearance to the lizards,
they have neither claws nor scales and their front feet have no
more than four toes, as compared with the lizard's five.

All salamanders avoid direct sun, many are nocturnal, and few
are capable of producing sound. Some forms are strictly aquatic;
others spend some time in the water and some time on land, after
having undergone a metamorphosis; and still others are entirely
terrestrial. And some secrete a potent poison, whereas others discharge a fluid that is mildly toxic and that irritates the mouth of a
predator or causes illness.

178

Mud Puppy,
Necturus maculosus

The number of salamanders in North America is greater than the number distributed throughout the rest of the world. The salamanders of North America belong to several families and number about 135 species.

MUD PUPPY, WATER DOG
Necturus

If you live in the North you probably refer to this tailed amphibian as a mud puppy; if you live in the South you undoubtedly call it a water dog. Both names are due in part to the mistaken belief that this aquatic salamander is capable of making a barking sound—a myth that came into being years ago and one that still prevails in some areas.

The scientific name of the northern species, the mud puppy, is *Necturus maculosus*. It is a dark brown salamander 8 to 12 inches long and distinguished by three sets of bushy red gills. It is a salamander that remains a larva all its life, frequenting rivers, lakes, ponds, and other permanent bodies of water in much of the East—

from north of the Great Lakes on south throughout the drainage systems of the Mississippi and Hudson rivers.

During the day the mud puppy secretes itself in the bottom mud or beneath a flat rock. It comes out of hiding as soon as twilight falls, and moves through the water at depths of 4 to 8 feet. It swims leisurely, using its long, flattened tail as a fin. As it swims it is on the lookout for such prey as small fishes, adult and larval water insects, and other small aquatic animals. It also prowls along the bottom as it searches for crayfish.

Before settling down for a dormant winter interlude, the mud puppy mates. The following spring the female discharges tiny round eggs that are yellow and about ¼ inch in diameter. The eggs are enclosed in a gelatinous mass, and may be attached to stones and rocks or placed beneath them. Sometimes they are deposited in a sandy nest exposed to plenty of sunlight. A female often lays more than one hundred eggs; she protects them by staying in the vicinity of the nest until they hatch. This takes forty to sixty days.

At hatching a young mud puppy has an overall length of ¾ inch; at the end of ten weeks, it measures 1½ inches; and by the time it is full grown it may measure as much as 18 inches, though a more usual length is one foot. It matures in five to seven years and has a life span reported as twenty years.

The Gulf Coast water dog (*N. m. beyeri*) is smaller than its northern relatives; it measures 6 to 8¾ inches from end to end. It appears lighter in color than the northern form because its dark skin is patterned by innumerable tan spots. This aquatic salamander frequents streams emptying into the Gulf of Mexico on a range that extends from Alabama to southeastern Texas.

HELLBENDER
Cryptobranchus alleganiensis

The dark brown or black hellbender has a wrinkled skin that appears far too large. It is further distinguished by a broad, flattened head, by a lack of gill ruffles, and by four stubby legs and a long tail that accounts for nearly one-third of its entire length. And the thick skin is exceedingly slimy.

This salamander frequents streams and rivers in the eastern United States from southern New York to Alabama and west to central Missouri. It likes water in which there is a noticeable current and plenty of shelter such as that afforded by large rocks, river debris, and stumps or snags. It is inactive during the day, staying quietly near or under some object that provides shelter. It hunts by night, prowling along the bottom in search of crayfish, aquatic insects, and worms. It swims from one hunting ground to another by flexing its long body and tail so that it moves ahead in a series of wriggles.

This salamander often seizes a baited hook. Many fishermen, upon pulling in a hellbender, cut the line and lose their gear rather than take the animal off the hook. They do so because there is a widespread belief that the hellbender is poisonous. This is not true, though it is unpleasant to handle because it is so slimy.

In the fall the male prepares a small nest by scooping out a hollow sheltered by a rock, then lures a female to it and induces her to deposit her eggs. Sometimes she discharges as many as two thousand in long strings. The male fertilizes the eggs by discharging milt. Once the last egg is released, the female leaves. The male protects the nest for about ten days or two weeks, eating a few eggs in the meantime.

A hellbender in the larval stage has external gills. They are very much in evidence at nine months, when this amphibian is about 2½ inches long. By the time it is a year old, the gills are less evident and the legs have started to develop. When it reaches the age of two years it measures 6 inches and the gills have almost disappeared. At the end of three or four years the hellbender is mature and measures one foot, though it continues to grow until it may measure as much as 20 inches. Record lengths for this thoroughly aquatic salamander are 22 and 29 inches.

AMPHIUMA, "CONGO EEL"
Amphiuma means

The so-called Congo eel is not an animal introduced from the Congo, nor is it an eel. It is a dark brown or black amphibian with two pairs of ridiculously small legs that end in feet equipped with two, three, or four toes. And it is one of the salamanders capable of inflicting a nasty bite.

The reason for its popular name is that this salamander was thought to have been brought here from Africa during the days of the slave trade. This name, and such others as "lamper eel" and "ditch eel," are still used in various regions, though the generic name *Amphiuma* is coming into use as a popular name. The name "Congo eel" is also applied to the salamanders known as sirens.

The Congo eel frequents a wide variety of watery habitats throughout the coastal plain from Virginia south into Florida. It is also found in the Mississippi Valley as far north as Missouri and west along the Gulf coast to southeastern Texas. It spends most of its time in the water, but on rainy nights it often wriggles overland from one pool, pond, or other water area to another. It usually lurks on the bottom, secreting itself in the mud or hiding among broken rocks or other bottom litter. It waits, with its somewhat pointed head thrust out, for crayfish or other prey to come along. In addition, it pursues frogs, small fishes, snakes, and, being cannibalistic, other amphiumas. According to some reports it often attacks by twisting around its victim in the manner of a snake and biting as it does so.

The mating season is in early July. The eggs are laid during August and September in nests scooped out under some sort of shelter. Though each egg is ejected singly, all are connected by a cord that often measures as much as 8 feet. Each embryo lies in a spiral position within its transparent cover. The female broods the eggs, staying coiled about them so that they are always warm and moist. As soon as the eggs hatch, she abandons them.

The Congo eel is born with three pairs of external gills. They are absorbed by the time it becomes an adult, and only branchial slits remain to show where they have been. The length of a full-grown Congo eel is 20 to 30 inches, and the life span of a captive specimen has been reported as twenty-six years.

The subspecies are the two-toed Amphiuma (*A. means means*) and the three-toed (*A. m. tridactylum*). The two-toed is usually smaller than the three-toed form, and is dark brown or black with a gray underside or venter. The three-toed Amphiuma is distinguished by a dark throat patch, a light gray venter, and a dark brown back.

SIRENS
Sirenidae

The sirens are eel-like salamanders of shallow waters. One species, the greater siren (*Siren lacertina*) frequents such waters on a range that starts in the vicinity of Washington, D. C., and extends to Florida. This salamander, measuring 20 to 30 inches from end to end, is distinguished by a pair of tiny front legs ending in feet with four toes. It also has three sets of yellow-orange gills—gills often so large and feathery that they completely cover the legs. The back is dark green, and the lighter underside is generously flecked with green or yellow.

Occasionally the greater siren eats quantities of the green filaments of algae, but it is usually carnivorous. Its diet includes such other water animals as crayfish and mollusks. In turn it is preyed upon by the rainbow snake (*Abastor erythrogrammus*), a glossy reptile striped in red and black, that frequents areas from Maryland to central Florida.

Another of these eel-like salamanders is the lesser siren (*S. intermedia*), a species that frequents shallow water throughout the Southeast, parts of Texas, and the lower Mississippi Valley. This siren is a species that estivates if necessary. During a drought, it burrows into the bottom mud, where it stays concealed in a state of actual suspended animation. It does not "come to" again until the rains are sufficiently heavy to refill the ditch or other dried-up area in which it was formerly active.

These two salamanders, often referred to as "mud eels," are reported to live as long as twenty-five years. *S. lacertina* has an end-to-end measurement of 20 to 30 inches. The dark brown or bluish-black lesser siren (*S. intermedia*) has an overall measurement of 7 to 20 inches.

The dwarf or mud sirens are salamanders of the extreme Southeast. You are sure to find these eel-like animals, with tiny forelegs and external gills, wherever there are water hyacinths. These lavender-flowering aquatic plants afford food and shelter for the narrow-striped form (*Pseudobranchus striatus axanthus*) and related forms.

This dwarf siren, measuring 5 to 8 inches, has a long, slender body. The head ends in a rounded snout and each foot is equipped with three toes. Its stripes are so indistinct that it appears a solid gray-black. The four other dwarf sirens, all three-toed forms, have distinct stripes. Like the narrow-striped siren they are subspecies, and they are known popularly as the broad-striped, the slender, the Everglades, and the Gulf hummock dwarf sirens. Their scientific names are *Pseudobranchus striatus striatus*, *P. s. spheniscus*, *P. s. belli*, and *P. s. lustricolus*.

EASTERN NEWTS
Diemictylus

From the large boas, to the little neute;
As well as birds, or the foure-footed beasts,
Came to the Arke their Hostry as Noe's guests.
MICHAEL DRAYTON

The "little neute" belongs to a large family known scientifically as the Salamandridae. In eastern North America there are three species and several subspecies. One is the red-spotted newt (*Diemictylus viridescens viridescens*). This salamander is found on a range that begins in the Maritime Provinces of Canada and extends south throughout most of the eastern half of the United States, to the tip of Florida in the East and to the eastern half of Texas in the West.

The male red-spotted newt conducts his courtship during the fall, winter, or spring. During this interval the tail, a finlike affair, is more than usually conspicuous. As soon as the courtship is over, the male expels a spermatophore, a jellylike mass containing sperm. The female collects this to fertilize the hundred or more oval eggs she deposits on the underwater parts of stems or leaves of aquatic plants. The eggs hatch in twenty or thirty days, and the water surrounding the stem or leaf on which the eggs were deposited is then filled with tiny, gilled larvae, measuring less than ¼ inch in length. The forelegs appear at the end of two days and the hind legs sprout at the end of three.

By the time the larval form of the red-spotted newt is three months old, it has lost its gills and is about one inch in length. Now, it is at a point in its life when it is ready to come ashore. This land interval last three or four years, and is an interval when the red-spotted salamander is known as the red eft.

The red eft, with an overall measurement of 1 to 3 inches, lives up to its name. It is a bright orange-red, dotted along the back with two rows of vermilion spots ringed in black. While it is on land its skin is rougher and not nearly so slimy as that of other salamanders. As it darts about on its moist and shady home range, it is seldom the victim of a predator. For the secretion of the skin glands is toxic and irritates the mucous membranes. Thus, with little to fear, it scampers over the forest floor in search of insects of all kinds, including mosquitoes. In its own small way, therefore, the red eft functions as a natural control of insect pests.

The efts spending their first year on land and those that came out of the water the year before gather together in the fall. They wander over the forest floor in search of places to hibernate. They finally settle down to overwinter under accumulations of fallen leaves, branches and logs, or other natural litter. Sometimes the adult aquatic forms come out of the water to pass the winter on land.

Some red-spotted newts bypass the land stage and become adults without leaving the water. But those that spend some time on land have to return to water to become adults. The return takes place in the spring or the fall, and is in the form of a mass migration. For all the red efts converge at one spot, then move toward a nearby pond or stream. These migrations occur only when the temperature is mild.

The aquatic adult is an olive-green, greenish-brown, or yellow-brown creature. The underside, or venter, is yellow and dotted with spots of black. The broad swimming tail has a finlike projection. In its aquatic adult form, the red-spotted newt is often active throughout the year—even if its habitat is ice-coated. Sometimes one rests motionless on or near the bottom; at other times, it swims slowly along; and at still other times, it crawls over the bottom.

This salamander eats almost any small aquatic animal. Some of the creatures in its diet are mollusks, worms, newly hatched amphibians, and insects in their larval form. It also eats quantities of frogs' eggs, and is therefore often considered an enemy of frogs.

The red-spotted newt is one of our long-lived salamanders, with a known life span of seven years.

Other eastern newts are the peninsula (*D. v. piaropicola*) of peninsular Florida, distinguished by a dark dorsum and a yellow venter spotted with black. This newt is found in various fresh-water habitats, including canals choked with water hyacinth. The broken-striped newt (*D. v. dorsalis*) is a salamander of the Carolina coastal plain. Its popular name comes from the fact that the black-bordered red stripe on the head and back is usually broken in one and sometimes in two places.

A third eastern newt is the central (*D. v. louisianensis*), a slender subspecies found from the Lake Superior area as far south as South Carolina in the East and eastern Texas in the West. Then there is the striped newt (*D. v. perstriatus*), which frequents shallow waters on a range that includes southern Georgia and northern Florida. And finally there is the black-spotted newt, distinguished by the large black spots that give it its popular name. This species, known scientifically as *D. meridionalis*, is limited to the wet and water areas of southernmost Texas and northern Mexico.

WESTERN OR PACIFIC NEWTS
Taricha

The western or Pacific newts are represented by a number of species and subspecies whose combined ranges extend coastwise from southern Canada as far south as the vicinity of the Mexican border. One of these western newts is *Taricha torosa*. Though its accepted common name is the California newt, it is frequently referred to as the Pacific Coast newt.

The livery of the California newt is a reddish or dark brown on the upper side and a bright yellow or orange below. It has a somewhat rounded snout, four well-developed legs, and a long, laterally flattened tail, with the tail accounting for half the entire body length of 6 or 7 inches. This type of tail facilitates swimming. During its land interludes, the skin is usually rough and warty, whereas in the water the skin tends to be much smoother.

By the middle of January the California newt is ready to breed in the clear, sparkling pools that dot its range. The male precedes the female to the water. How much of its life is spent in water and how much is passed on land is uncertain. For as Gayle Pickwell, Professor of Zoology at San Jose State College, once wrote, "Many things in the life story of the newt are yet to be learned, and this matter of his stay in water and his stay on land is one of them."

Once the California newt takes to the water, it develops swimming fins on both the upper and under surfaces of its tail. A male swims around and around in the breeding water until a female arrives. A mating then occurs in the water. This species, like all other western newts, is one in which the fertilization of the eggs takes place within the body.

When the time comes to deposit her eggs, the female moves into the shallow water at the edge of the pond or pool. The eggs are round, about ⅛ inch in diameter, and two-colored. The upper half is a light brown, whereas the lower part is white. A dozen or so eggs are enclosed in a good-sized capsule of jelly. As the embryonic salamander within an egg starts to grow, the egg itself becomes elongated. At the end of two or three weeks, the outline of the newt-to-be is visible, and in a month or six weeks, the young amphibian is ready to break out of its individual egg.

As a water creature the young newt has a set of feathery gills, by means of which it breathes. Before it leaves the water the gills are absorbed and it must then rise to the surface regularly in order to breath by means of its newly developed lungs. A young newt is not the uniform reddish or dark brown of the adult; it also differs because it is a striped creature whose skin is dotted with black. Its forelegs appear at the time of hatching, and its hind legs are in evidence shortly thereafter.

Immediately after hatching, a young newt is preyed upon by a number of water insects, including the backswimmer, and by other, older newts. In turn a recently hatched newt probably feeds on minute insects such as the water flea, and upon the newly dead of its own kind.

The California newt spends about one year in the water after hatching. It passes the next two years on land, wandering over the damp and leafy forest floor of its home area. When it is three years old, it is mature and ready to breed, and from then on it alternates periods on land with intervals in the water.

MOLE SALAMANDERS
Ambystoma

Among the many mole salamanders in North America is one known scientifically as *Ambystoma tigrinum tigrinum*. The popular name of this 8-inch amphibian is the eastern tiger salamander, for it is encased in a livery of dark brown or black spotted with yellow. Sometimes the spots are so numerous and so large that they form irregular bands. The underside has a marbled effect because it is a combination of light and dark yellow-brown.

This species, like the other mole salamanders, spends most of its time underground. It makes a burrow in soft earth on a range that extends along the Atlantic side of the Appalachian Mountains from New York to Florida. West of these mountains, it is found from Ohio south to the Gulf coast and north as far as southern Canada.

The tiger salamander of the North is ready to breed by January, whereas the southern form often breeds as late as March. A male worms his way out of the ground and goes overland to the nearest water. As soon as the female arrives, there is a courtship that includes love play. When this is concluded the male releases a spermatophore to fertilize the eggs. Shortly thereafter the female releases twenty-five to seventy-six eggs (usually about thirty-eight) encased in a jellylike mass measuring 3 by 4 inches. The eggs hatch in twelve to eighteen days, depending upon environmental conditions. The larva that emerges is less than ¾ inch long. At the end of ten or twelve weeks, the transformation into adult form occurs.

During a life span of ten to sixteen years, the tiger salamander feeds on small earthbound animals or those available when it comes out on rainy nights to prowl around on its water-washed territory. If surprised above ground at daybreak, it scurries to take refuge under old boards or any other convenient cover.

Some tiger salamanders never develop into the land form. These individuals grow to a large size, eventually become sexually mature, but still retain their gills. Such individuals are known technically as "neotenic." This zoological term means that the period of immaturity is indefinitely prolonged. The salamander in the Valley of Mexico that does not assume the adult form, but which can breed nonetheless, has a special name in Mexico. Here, many years ago, this form was given the name *axolotl*. The axolotls from the lakes in and around Mexico City are considered edible, and are sold in the markets of this city.

The strange behavior of the axolotl upon being shipped was noted by Thomas Barbour of the Museum of Comparative Zoology at Harvard University. In *Reptiles And Amphibians, Their Habits and Adaptations* (1926), he wrote:

Yale University, however, found on having "axoltols" sent from certain lakes in New Mexico that the mere capture and shipment was sufficient stimulus or perhaps shock, so that they began to transform at once and on reaching New Haven soon assumed the adult or Ambystoma form.

Some other members of the family Ambystomidae, widespread in the United States, include the spotted salamander (*A. maculatum*), This species, measuring 6 to 7 inches in overall length, has a row of bright yellow spots on each side, extending from the eyes almost to the end of the tail.

The spotted salamander lives out its life span of twenty-odd years on a home area within an extensive range. For it is found throughout southern Canada from the vicinity of the Great Lakes to the Atlantic seaboard, then south in the eastern United States to Florida and south from the Great Lakes area into eastern Texas. It frequents moist, woodsy areas, where it feeds on earthworms and on insects and their larvae.

The movement of the spotted salamander to a breeding area is likely to take place in the early spring after the first warm rains.

Such rains apparently trigger all the individuals within a given area, for the trek to the breeding pond or pool assumes the proportions of a mass migration. As soon as the male completes his courtship, which includes such byplay as tapping the female's body with his tail, he discharges a jellylike spermatophore that fertilizes the hundred or so eggs expelled by the female.

After an interval of incubation, the eggs hatch larvae, measuring about ½ inch. At the end of three months—immediately before transforming into the adult form—the larvae may be as long as 3 inches. During the next year of its life—the one after transformation—a young spotted salamander grows another 3 inches. From then on growth ceases for some, whereas others may grow slowly until they are 7 or more inches from one end to the other. A record length for one of these salamanders is 9 inches.

Another of the Ambystomidae is the Jefferson salamander (*A. jeffersonianum*). This long-toed, slender species is sometimes known as the blue-spotted salamander because its dark brown skin is occasionally flecked with blue. It frequents woodsy areas edging swamps and streams on a range that includes southeastern Canada and the New England states and those around the Great Lakes.

In the United States the range of the Jefferson salamander overlaps that of the marbled (*A. opacum*). A small species, the marbled

Marbled Salamander,
Ambystoma opacum

salamander is found from southern New York, then on south into northern Florida, and west into eastern Texas.

Throughout this area it frequents a home range that may be on predominantly moist terrain or an land that is extremely sandy. It is also found on hillsides that afford little or no moisture.

After a mating that occurs in the autumn, the female expels her eggs in a depression sufficiently deep to hold and retain water. She guards her eggs until enough rain falls to cover the clutch. If the autumn happens to be a season of drought, the eggs do not hatch until the first warm rains of the following spring. The eggs in a clutch may number as few as fifty or as many as two hundred. And the incubation period may be as short as fifteen days or as long as two hundred or more days.

The larval stage of the marbled salamander lasts five or six months. At this time it is a mottled brown. Once it transforms, it is a creature with a dull brown or black back, whose somberness is relieved by an occasional light fleck. The female is marked with gray; this distinguishes her from the male, whose corresponding marks are all-white.

The record length attained by *Ambystoma opacum* is 5 inches. A more usual length for this chunky little species is 3½ or 4½ inches.

These mole salamanders, and such others as the ringed, the reticulated flatwoods, and the small-mouthed, are frequently used as laboratory animals. Many of them make good pets, and thrive in terrariums in which there are several inches of moist earth and other features that simulate their natural habitat. Though they prefer live earthworms and other live invertebrates, they sometimes learn to feed on bits of raw meat.

SPRING SALAMANDERS
Gyrinophilus

The Great Smoky Mountains are in an area second only to the Pacific Northwest with regard to the amount of yearly precipitation. These eastern mountains are in an ancient region watered by numerous brooks, streams, and rivulets. And the mountain forests of the area—the southern Appalachians—are frequented by at least twenty-seven species of salamanders.

One of the salamanders found within the confines of Great Smoky Mountains National Park is the reddish or salmon-colored mountain spring salamander (*Gyrinophilus danielsi*). This salamander, of 5 to 7 inches, is found at heights of more than 2,500 feet. It frequents rushing mountain brooks and the spray-dashed edges along such brooks. It is also a creature of clear, cold springs, and areas in the forest where there is seepage.

The mountain spring salamander, formerly known as the purple mountain salamander, secretes itself under stones. Sometimes in turning over a stone, you catch sight of one of these vividly colored amphibians—indigenous to eastern North America. Occasionally, if you are fortunate, you may see a hundred or more of them at one spot. Dr. Willis King and his wife had such an experience. The Doctor reports it in "A Survey of the Herpetology of Great Smoky Mountains National Park," the *American Midland Naturalist* (v. 21, pp. 531–582):

On the night of April 20, 1937, Mrs. King and I were driving from Gatlinburg to Waynesville between 8 and 9 P.M. It was a warm foggy night, following a period of showers. On Newfound Gap, Tennessee side, between 3,500 and 5,000 feet elevation we saw at least 200 salamanders of this species crawling about on the road. They could be seen at considerable distance because of the contrast of their light bodies on the black surface of the road, but even more striking was the reflection from their eyes. The presence of so many of these comparatively uncommon animals made the observation all the more interesting.

An explanation for this congregation is that during or immediately after a rainfall the surface of such a road is both warm and wet—a combination that attracts earthworms and other small invertebrates. In turn the prevalence of food brings predators in the form of the mountain spring salamander and other amphibians of the area. Of course feeding in such a spot is a hazard because there is no protection. A salamander is often seized by a screech owl because such prey is easy to catch without the hindrance of trees. Thus, in a way, the mountain spring salamander, whose habits are little known, is a victim of its predilection for "easy pickin's."

Some other salamanders in this group are the Kentucky cave salamander (*G. lutescens*), a small pinkish species dotted with black along each side. Its range is in southwestern Virginia and southern Ohio. Then there is the Blue Ridge spring salamander (*G. d. danielsi*), a red subspecies, whose stripes are a distinct black. And in southeastern Ohio there is a spring salamander named for the state. This is *G. porphyriticus inagnoscus* that has a reddish back with a mottled design down the center. These are but ten of the spring salamanders, a genus that occurs only in eastern North America.

DUSKY SALAMANDERS
Desmognathus

Another salamander of the Great Smokies and nearby mountainous regions is known scientifically as *Desmognathus wrighti*. The popular name for this 2-inch, bronze-colored amphibian is the pigmy salamander. The first specimens of *D. wrighti* were discovered in the Smokies, where it is found at altitudes between 3,500 and 6,500 feet.

The pigmy salamander, strictly a land form, passes the day secreted under the litter of the forest floor. It ventures out at night, sometimes climbing up the trunk of a tree to a height of 6 or 7 feet. And the trees on which it climbs are those of high altitudes, such as the Fraser fir and the red spruce.

A close relative of the pigmy salamander is *Desmognathus fuscus*, common throughout the East on a range that extends from southern Canada to Mississippi, and westward to Illinois. The popular name of this short-bodied species is the dusky salamander. It is distinguished by a light line running diagonally from the eye to the mouth. It has a long tail, hind legs that exceed the length of the forelegs, and a tongue attached to the forward margin of the mouth. The color of the back is usually a uniform black or yellow-brown. The underside is paler than the dorsum.

Throughout its range the dusky salamander frequents a home area in the vicinity of perennially running water. During fall and winter all forms—adults; partly grown, air-breathing young; and gilled larvae—are semiactive. And during fall or spring the male courts the female, following this premating behavior by releasing a spermatophore.

Once the female secures the means by which her eggs are fertilized, she is ready to expel them. She lays her clutch of creamy-white eggs from June to September. The eggs, ⅛ inch in diameter and bunched like grapes, are deposited in a moist place on land. The female usually guards the clutch for about eight weeks, or until they hatch into larvae measuring ½ inch. The larval forms remain on land for fifteen days; then they enter the water to stay in this environment for the next eight or ten months.

At the end of this water interlude the larva transforms into an air-breathing adult measuring about one inch in length. Since the dusky salamander is a lungless species, respiration is accomplished through the skin and the mouth. Now it is ready to leave the water and take up life on land.

The dusky salamander is mature at the end of two years, when it measures approximately 2 inches from end to end. The size of this salamander varies: some are fully grown at 2½ inches; others may continue to grow until they are as long as 4½ inches; and occasionally there are those that attain a length of 5 inches.

This salamander is a nocturnal species. It prowls around in search of such prey as earthworms, slugs, snails, spiders, and insects of all kinds. It also eats some vegetation. As it hunts, it is likely to be preyed on by the mountain spring salamander and by mammal predators including the raccoon.

The dusky and pigmy salamanders are but two of the many species and subspecies belonging to a family, the Plethodontidae, found from southern Canada to northern South America. In the United States they are most abundant in the southern Appalachians, where heavy precipitation, numerous waterways, plenty of shelter, and an abundance of food create an ideal environment.

RED and MUD SALAMANDERS
Pseudotriton

Sometimes the bait industry is responsible for the unintentional distribution of certain salamanders. One of these salamanders—all called "spring lizards" by the men who sell them—is the northern red salamander (*Pseudotriton ruber ruber*). It is fairly common in the East from southern New York to northern Alabama.

The northern red salamander hatches from an egg deposited in the autumn. The egg is one of fifty laid in a series of small clusters glued to the undersides of rocks in rapidly flowing water. The larva that hatches in October, or even later, remains inactive during the winter. When spring comes, it is about one inch long and its livery is a greenish brown.

This species spends the first three and a half years of its life in water. At the end of this period, it is about 4 inches long and the gills have started to shrink. Now it starts to breathe through the skin and the throat membrane, and now it assumes its young adult coloring—red, coral-red, or reddish orange. Its back is liberally sprinkled with round black dots, and the iris of the eye is usually yellow.

As an adult, the northern red salamander lives on land. It shelters under mosses, rocks, stones, and other hiding places on a home range that is always wet or moist. And on land it continues to grow until it measures 4¼ to 6 inches from the tip of its snout to the end of its black-tipped tail. As this species of salamander ages, its vivid color fades to a purple-brown, and brown or black spots appear on the underside.

The northern red salamander is one of several in the genus *Pseudotriton*. This group includes the eastern mud salamander (*P. montanus montanus*), a brown-eyed species that frequents a range from southern New Jersey to northeastern Georgia. A still more southerly species is the rusty mud salamander (*P. montanus floridanus*) of southern Georgia and northern Florida. As its popular name suggests, it is a creature of muddy areas dotted by pools and puddles of water. And then there is the black-chinned red salamander (*P. ruber schencki*), a small species with a decidedly black chin patch. It is found high in the southern Blue Ridge Mountains, sometimes at elevations of more than five thousand feet. It, like others of its kind, is native only to the eastern part of North America.

WOODLAND SALAMANDERS
Plethodon

The woodland salamanders are found only in North America. Among the many species and subspecies in this group are the slimy salamander (*Plethodon glutinosus*) of the East, and the western red-backed salamander (*P. vehiculum*) that occurs from British Columbia to western Oregon. These salamanders, both in the East and in the West, vary greatly in size and slenderness.

Inland you will find such woodland salamanders as the Ouachita red-backed (*P. cinereus serratus*) of mountain forests of Arkansas and Oklahoma, and the species known as the zig-zig salamander (*P. dorsalis dorsalis*) found in rocky areas from central Indiana to an area embracing the western side of the Blue Ridge Mountains.

The slimy salamander of the East lives up to its name, for its skin glands secrete a substance that adheres to the skin like glue. The amphibian that secretes this slime is, in its adult form, a long, slender creature encased in a livery of black flecked with pinpoints of white. The location of the white spots varies from one individual to another. Sometimes they are on the forward part of the body; at other times, they are scattered along the sides; and occasionally they are so few as to be barely discernible. The underside is gray, and the feet are fawn. The forefeet have four toes, whereas the hind feet are equipped with five.

The range of the slimy salamander extends from southeastern Canada south throughout the greater part of the East to central Florida. There is an extension of the range westward to Wisconsin, Missouri, Oklahoma, and Texas. Throughout this range the slimy salamander and such subspecies as the white-throated (*P. glutinosus albagula*), *the Carolina (P. g. chlorobryonis), and the Florida (P. g. grobmani*) frequent territories that are moist and well forested.

The slimy salamander is often found in a shady ravine through which trickles a rivulet. There was a ravine such as this near my home in Troy, New York, in which I played and where I caught slimy salamanders while damming the rivulet. As I recall the salamanders of "my ravine," I have a distinct impression of glistening wetness, but no memory of their slime adhering to my hands.

During its active season this species feeds on earthworms, centipedes, and insects, including hard-shelled beetles, ants of all kinds, and many of the true bugs, some of which are downright smelly. It seeks its prey at night or immediately after heavy daytime rains. Most of its daylight hours, however, are passed hidden beneath rocks and stones, old boards and rotting logs, or buried under leafy debris. And during midwinter there is a quiescent interval when this amphibian is "dead to the world."

Though the life history of the slimy salamander is far from being a complete matter of record, it is believed to mate in the fall, with the female depositing her eggs during late winter or early spring. The white eggs, ¼ inch in diameter, are laid in clusters. The nest may be a crevice in a cave, a damp and rotting log, or a bed of damp moss. Some females guard the eggs; others do not.

The woodland salamander does not undergo an aquatic larval stage, but emerges from the egg in adult form. The flecks that dot a juvenile are often golden, rather than white or silvery as are those on mature adults. The usual length attained is about 6 inches, though some individuals may be as short as 4¾ inches and others as long as 7 inches.

Another common woodland salamander of the East is the red-backed (*P. cinereus cinereus*), a slender species that has two color phases. Some individuals are red or plum and have a red or gray stripe on the back. Others are gray or black. The underside of either color phase is a mottled black-and-white.

The red-backed salamander is a terrestrial species that frequents the woods and forests on a range that includes southeastern Canada, New England, the Great Lakes area, then extends south in the East to Georgia and Alabama, and west to Oklahoma. Within this area, it hides by day beneath any convenient debris on its home range. It comes out at night to hunt for insects and other small live prey, sometimes catching its victim by a lightning-like forward thrust of its tongue.

The period of dormancy for the red-backed salamander is not long. It has been found feeding in southern Michigan as late as the first part of December and as early as the end of March. Sometimes it mates before becoming inactive, or it may wait until it rouses in the spring.

The female deposits a dozen or so white eggs, jelly-coated and measuring about ⅕ inch in diameter, in a single cluster. The nest may be in a hollow log or under a stone. The female broods the eggs, in which the larval stage is passed. The young, an inch long at hatching, retain their larval gills for only a short time. By the time one is two years old, it has an overall length of 1 ½ inches. And when fully grown one may measure as much as 5 inches, with the male usually shorter than the female.

BROOK SALAMANDERS
Eurycea

The various brook salamanders occur mostly in eastern North America. Some live up to their group name because they spend the greater part of their lives in springs, shallow brooks, and the moisture-filled areas around or along such waters. Others lead a much more terrestrial life, though they take to the water from time to time. And then there are still others so aquatic that they never leave the water.

The northern two-lined salamander (*Eurycea bislineata bislineata*) is fairly typical of this group. It is a yellow-backed species, though the basic color may have a brown, bronze, or greenish cast. There are two dark lines along each side from eye to tail. And the underside is yellow.

This species is found on a range that extends from southern Canada throughout most of the eastern United States as far south as Virginia. Some time during the fall, a male of this area courts a female, then deposits a spermatophore. The female picks this up to fertilize her eggs. In the spring—late May in Connecticut—the female expels small clutches. The eggs are translucent and measure about ⅕ inch in diameter They are attached to the underside of a rock or some other protective object in swiftly flowing water. They hatch in about ten weeks, and the larvae that emerge are slender and yellow, and have an overall length of ¼ or ½ inch. For a few hours they cling to what is left of the egg casings.

At the end of two weeks the larvae have developed their legs, and by the time they are 2 inches long they have started to lose their gills. Now the transformation to adult form is slow, and will not be complete until the end of two years. One of these salamanders seldom exceeds 4 inches in length, though there is a record of one measuring 4¼ inches.

The northern two-lined salamander often forages during the day. It feeds on small aquatic insects, spiders, and other small water animals. During the winter it frequently feeds as usual, but moves to deeper water to do so. Or it may spend the winter months secreted under litter on land.

From northern Carolina to northern Florida, the southern two-lined salamander frequents the coastal plain and piedmont regions. It is a subspecies known scientifically as *Eurycea bislineata cirrigera* because the downward projections from the nostrils (the cirri) are so pronounced.

The Blue Ridge two-lined salamander (*E. b. wilderae*) is found from southwestern Virginia to northern Georgia. It is a vividly colored and marked form of high altitudes—elevations of two thousand feet or more. It frequents springs and rivulets and the areas immediately surrounding them.

The most terrestrial members of this group have exceedingly long tails; they measure more than one-half of the individual's total length. One such is the long-tailed salamander (*E. longicauda longicauda*), yellowish in hue and distinguished by vertical markings on the tail. This 4-to-6-inch salamander frequents cave entrances, hides under rocks and stones, crawls into or hides beneath rotting logs, or shelters under any other sort of protection available along the banks of waterways. Its range is from southern New York to Alabama and Kentucky.

Two other salamanders of this group, the Oklahoma (*E. tynerensis*) and the Texas (*E. neotenes*), are neotenic forms. They retain gills throughout life. Each frequents creeks, springs, wells, and other small bodies of water on a restricted range. That of the grayish Oklahoma salamander is a tri-state area—a part of northeastern Oklahoma and parts of Arkansas and Missouri. The light-brown Texas salamander is a species of the rocky area of central Texas.

In this same group are two salamanders that live within caves or just back of their entrances. One is the cave salamander (*E. lucifuga*), a reddish species that measures 4 to 6 inches in length. It is a creature of limestone areas from Virginia to Oklahoma. The second cave-dweller is the dark-sided salamander (*E. longicauda melanopleura*). It is found throughout the Ozarks and nearby areas. It has, as might be expected from its popular name, a dark stripe along each side of the body. When fully grown it sometimes measures nearly 7 inches from end to end, though a more usual length is 3 to 5 inches.

SOME OTHER NORTH AMERICAN SALAMANDERS

One of the places where you can see a "ghost lizard" is the Smithsonian Institution in Washington, D. C. Twenty-one such "lizards" were presented to the Smithsonian by Dr. C. G. Goodchild of Southwest Missouri State College, Springfield, Missouri. These white or pinkish-white creatures are said to be among the rarest animals in the world. For, so far as is known, they occur only in the limestone regions of the southern United States.

"Ghost lizard" is a regional name for the grotto or Ozark salamander (*Typhlotriton spelaeus*). It is one of the blind salamanders, for in its adult form its eyes are vestigial. In its larval form, it frequents mountain springs and brooks. It is then similar to the larvae of many other salamanders; it has eyes that function, external gills, and a tail distinguished by a high fin. Its color is basically gray, overcast either with a purple or brown hue, and the sides are either streaked or spotted.

As an adult it lives in deep wells, in underground streams, or in those in caves and caverns. Here it becomes white and nearly translucent; its eyes no longer function, and the lids partially or completely fuse. The tail fin also disappears. Now it is a creature of darkness, and remains a blind cave-dweller for the rest of its life.

The Texas blind salamander (*Typhlomolge rathbuni*), another of these odd animals, is found in the limestone escarpments of central Texas. It is a 4-inch species that never takes on the adult form. It retains a set of feathery pink gills throughout its life. Probably the rarest of all the blind salamanders in North America is *Haideotriton wallacei*. This species, distinguished by large pink gills, has a more rounded snout than the other forms. Its common name is the Georgia blind salamander. For years there was only one known specimen. Now others have been discovered.

Other North American salamanders restricted in range are a part of the fauna along the Pacific coast. One of these is the painted salamander known scientifically as *Ensatina eschscholtzi picta*. This salamander and others in the same group occupy a long, narrow range that starts in British Columbia and extends as far south as San Diego County in California.

The painted salamander has a livery of red or black and one that is marked by yellow-orange blotches or stripes. Throughout its own particular range it frequents the floor of oak and evergreen forests. A second member of this western group is the slender or worm salamander (*Batrachoseps attenuatus*). It is a thin, wormlike species with an exceedingly long tail. The color of the skin is dark brown, with darker spots and streaks. This 4-inch salamander frequents the vicinity of rotting logs, spending much of its time secreted beneath such havens. The female lays her eggs beneath boards and rocks, and the young that emerge are miniatures of the adults. And there is one member of this group that occurs only on the island of Santa Catalina. This is *Batrachoseps pacificus catalinae*.

A salamander restricted to a small area in the East is the green (*Aneides aeneus*), a climbing species. It frequents damp crevices of cliffs in the Appalachian Mountains. The livery of this lively, 4-inch creature is a dark green, with a light green or yellow underside. It scampers about over its rocky range on feet equipped with broadened toes, sometimes taking to the trees of its neighborhood.

Another climbing salamander is a species of the West. This is the tree or arboreal salamander, whose scientific name is *Aneides lugubris*. It is distinguished by a light brown dorsum and a pale brown venter. This salamander of the Pacific coast frequents tree cavities that are wet enough to be called watersoaked. And in trying to catch one be wary, for its teeth are sharp enough to inflict a bite that draws blood.

The range of the climbing salamanders in the West starts as far north as British Columbia. Here, you will find the clouded or rusty salamander (*A. ferreus*), a 4½-inch creature whose range extends as far south as Mendocino County, California. The black salamander (*A. flavipunctatus*) is found from Klamath County, Oregon, and on south to the lower border of Santa Cruz County, California. This species, sometimes dotted with silver or yellow, is distinguished by a flattened tail tip—a characteristic that sets it apart from all the others of its genus. The race of the arboreal salamander called the oak salamander (*A. l. lugubris*) frequents oak trees in central and southern California. It and the arboreal salamander have been given the specific name *lugubris* because the sharp-toothed upper jaw projects over the lower jaw. Another in this genus is *A. l. farallonensis* of the Farallon Islands, a rocky bird sanctuary twenty-six miles west of San Francisco.

Two members of the family Ambystomidae are restricted to the coast of California and the Pacific Northwest. One is the Pacific giant salamander (*Dicamptodon ensatus*), the largest of the western salamanders and one of the largest land species in the United States. It is a somewhat reddish-brown creature with a mottled back, measuring 9 to 12 inches from its rounded snout to the end of its thick tail.

The range of the Pacific giant salamander is coastal and coincides with that of the redwoods in California. It is also found in western Oregon and as far north as British Columbia. Adults are not common throughout the range, but the larval form is usually numerous in most of the streams watering the lands of its range.

The Olympic salamander (*Rhyacotriton olympicus*), known, too, as the mountain salamander, is the only member of its genus in the Pacific states. It is distinguished by a mid-dorsal groove that extends

Facing page: Pacific Giant Salamander, *Dicamptodon ensatus*

from the back of its head to the base of its tail. The color of its back is brown, whereas that of the underside is a bright yellow.

To find this far-from-common salamander, you will have to travel to the humid coniferous forests along the coast. Here, both the larval and adult forms frequent seepage that oozes from rock slides into clear streams. When this species is in the water, its body temperature is usually lower than that of its surroundings.

The Olympic salamander lays its eggs in the water. During May or June the female deposits three to fifteen eggs, one at a time, on the underside of a rock or stone. A hatchling from one of these eggs develops eventually into an adult with a smooth skin and one that measures no more than 3½ inches at its greatest length.

An unusual salamander with an uneven distribution is *Hemidactylium scutatum*. Most salamanders have five toes on each hind foot, but *scutatum* has only four. This peculiarity is the reason for the common name, four-toed salamander.

In eastern North America it usually occurs where there is sphagnum moss. As an adult it establishes itself on land, but as a larva it passes an interlude in the water. During her land sojourn, the female lays her eggs in a damp and mossy nest at the very edge of the water. She broods them for about two months. Upon hatching the young take to the water, where they stay about six weeks. They then come ashore to complete the transformation to adult form.

A full-grown four-toed salamander measures about 2½ inches. Though the male is smaller than the female, he has the longer tail. The color of the dorsum is brown or red, whereas that of the venter is white marked with black spots.

The four-toed salamander seems to be gregarious when it hibernates. F. N. Blanchard wrote in *Copeia* (1933, No. 4, p. 216) about those he found in southern Michigan during early November. Eighteen of these salamanders were tucked into the cavities of a rotting log or beneath the leaves near by. And immediately surrounding these hibernators nearly another two hundred were secreted beneath the leafy litter.

Another species with only four toes on the hind feet is the dwarf salamander (*Manculus quadridigitatus*). It is a salamander of the swamps on the coastal plain from the Carolinas to central Florida and west into Texas. It is dark-skinned, with a dark brown or black stripe down the back and a greenish underside. It seldom exceeds a length of 3 inches.

The last of our rare or regional species is the Mount Lyell salamander (*Hydromantes platycephalus*). It is unusual because the four toes of its front feet and the five on the hind are webbed. It was first discovered in 1915 at an altitude of 10,000 feet on Mount Lyell, a granite peak of more than 13,000 feet southwest of Donohue Pass in Yosemite National Park. The discovery of this salamander in the United States was startling because at that time the only other known members of the genus were found in the mountains of Sardinia and in the French and Italian Alps.

The Mount Lyell salamander, the other rare or regional forms, and those that are more widespread and commonplace are all a part of the North American fauna. They are the tailed amphibians, part of a group that includes the frogs and the toads, the tailless amphibians. Together they constitute a class midway between the fishes and the reptiles, and are specialized descendants of a great group of more or less aquatic forms alive during the late Paleozoic and Triassic times.

IN CONCLUSION

The reptiles and amphibians of North America, and those of other continents too, are important in the way all wild things are important. They are also a living resource that needs protection and greater understanding to appreciate its true worth.

Today there is a concentrated effort by all forms of government —local, state, and federal—to set aside areas that furnish the sort of environments required by many forms of wildlife, including the alligator—a reptile protected by various southern states and now safe from hunters on Delta National Wildlife Refuge in Louisiana. Private organizations and individuals, too, have established many special areas reasonably free from factors that disturb natural habitats. One of these is Wildcat Mountain Natural Area in Virginia— a preserve of one thousand acres near Warrenton under the jurisdiction of The Nature Conservancy. Here I have seen black snakes, copperheads, and salamanders, as well as other forms of wildlife, in a plant and animal community that is reverting to a truly "wild" state.

Delta National Wildlife Refuge, Wildcat Mountain Natural Area, Wood Buffalo Park in northern Alberta, and other similar areas are havens for many forms of North American wildlife. In the plant and animal communities of such special areas, the reptiles and amphibians of the continent are the less spectacular forms of wildlife, yet these creatures, first lords of the land, are usually vital to the welfare of their respective communities.

APPENDIX

GLOSSARY

ANTERIOR: At or toward the front of the body.

AXOLOTL: Aztec word for large aquatic form of tiger salamander.

BOSS: Rounded hump; on toads, between the eyes, sometimes near end of snout.

CARAPACE: Bony or chitinous case covering back of animal; upper shell of turtle.

CHITIN: A horny substance.

CIRRI: Downward projections from nostrils.

CREPUSCULAR: Active at twilight or dusk.

DIURNAL: Active during daylight hours.

DORSAL: Of or pertaining to upper surface.

DORSUM: The back.

ECOLOGY: That branch of biology dealing with mutual relations between organisms and their environment; bionomics.

ESTIVATION: Inactive state during prolonged droughts or high temperatures.

FORM: A kind; a species or subspecies, distinct and identifiable.

GILLS: Breathing structures for removing oxygen from water.

HABITAT: Natural abode of plant or animal, especially the particular location where it normally grows or lives.

HEMOTOXIC: Affecting blood and circulatory system.

HERPETOLOGY: Science that deals with the structure, habits, and classification of reptiles and amphibians.

HERPTILE: Reptiles and amphibians collectively.

HIBERNATION: Prolonged, inactive state during low temperatures.

HOMOIOTHERMAL: Pertaining to animals in which the body temperature is constant; the so-called warm-blooded animals.

IMBRICATE: Having parts that overlap one another, like slates on a roof.

JACOBSON'S ORGAN: Sensory organ located in roof of mouth; used to detect odors.

KEEL: Ridgelike process down back of turtles; lengthwise ridge on dorsal scales of some snakes.

LARVA (–AE, pl.): Immature stage between egg and adult; tadpole, polliwog.

NEOTENY: Retention of larval body form throughout life, even after sexual maturity has been reached. (adj., NEOTENIC).

NEUROTOXIC: Affecting nerves and nervous system.

NOCTURNAL: Active at night.

OCELLI: Eyelike spots.

OVIPAROUS: Reproducing by eggs that develop *outside* the female's body.

OVOVIVIPAROUS: Reproducing by eggs that develop *within* the female's body.

PAROTOID: Large, external gland on shoulders of toads in genus *Bufo*.

PLASTRON: Undershell of turtle; sometimes hinged.

POIKILOTHERMAL: Pertaining to variable temperature of animals such as reptiles and amphibians, whose temperatures are influenced by external environment; the so-called cold-blooded animals.

POSTERIOR: At or toward the rear of the body.

RACE: A subspecies; a group within a species; a geographical subspecies.

SCUTE: External, enlarged scale on reptile; also called a plate.

SPERMATOPHORE: Gelatinous mass of male sperm.

SPINOSE: Full of spines, armed with spines.

TADPOLE: Young, or larva, of frog or toad.

TERRITORY: An area defended against intruders of same species.

TERRESTRIAL: Land-living.

TUBERCLE: Little, knobby projection.

TYMPANUM: Eardrum.

VENTER: Entire underside of animal.

VENTRAL: Of or pertaining to underside.

VIVIPAROUS: Giving birth to young developed within the body of the mother.

VOCAL SAC: Single or paired inflatable pouch on throat or side of neck of male frog or toad.

SUGGESTED READING AND REFERENCES

Amphibians and Reptiles of the Pacific States, by Gayle Pickwell. 236 pp., illus., index. Stanford University Press, Stanford, California. 1947.

Animal Life and Lore, by Osmond P. Breland, 416 pp., illus., index. Harper & Row, New York. 1963.

Animal Physiology, by Knut Schmidt-Nielsen. 118 pp., illus., index. Prentice-Hall, Inc., Englewood Cliffs, N. J. 1960. (Foundations of Modern Biology).

Complete Field Guide to American Wildlife: East, Central, and North, by Henry Hill Collins, Jr. 683 pp., illus., index. Harper & Row, New York. 1959.

Dinosaurs, by Edwin H. Colbert. 300 pp., illus., index. E. P. Dutton & Co., Inc., New York. 1961.

Dinosaur Quarry, The: Dinosaur National Monument, by John Good, Theodore E. White, and Gilbert E. Stucker. 46 pp., illus. National Park Service. Superintendent of Documents, U. S. Government Printing Office, Washington 25, D. C. 1958.

Field Book of Animals in Winter, by Ann Haven Morgan. 527 pp., illus., index. G. P. Putnam's Sons, New York. 1939.

Field Guide to Reptiles and Amphibians of Eastern North America, by Roger Conant. 366 pp., illus., index. Houghton Mifflin Company, Boston. 1958. (The Peterson Field Guide Series)

Fossil Amphibians and Reptiles, by W. E. Swinton. 118 pp., illus., index. British Museum (Natural History), London. 1958.

Learning and Instinct in Animals, by W. H. Thorpe. 493 pp., illus., index. Harvard University Press, Cambridge, Massachusetts. 1956.

Living Amphibians of the World, by Doris M. Cochran. 199 pp., illus., index. Doubleday & Company, Inc., Garden City, New York. 1961.

Mermaids and Mastodons, by Richard Carrington. 251 pp., illus., index. Rinehart and Company, Inc., New York. 1957.

New Salamander of the Genus Gyrinophilus *From the Southern Appalachians* (With One Plate), by M. B. Mittleman and Harry G. M. Jopson. Publication 3638, The Smithsonian Institution, Washington, D. C. 1941.

Natural History of North American Amphibians and Reptiles, The, by James A. Oliver. 358 pp., illus., index. D. Van Nostrand Company, Princeton. 1955.

North American Deserts, The, by Edmund C. Jaeger, with a chapter by Peveril Meigs. 308 pp., illus., index. Stanford University Press, Stanford, California. 1957.

Origin of Species and the Descent of Man, The, by Charles Darwin. 1,000 pp., index. The Modern Library, Random House, Inc., New York.

Poisonous Amphibians and Reptiles: Recognition and Bite Treatment, by Floyd Boys and Hobart M. Smith. 149 pp., illus., index. Charles C Thompson, Springfield, Illinois. 1959.

Reptiles of the World, by Raymond L. Ditmars. 321 pp., with 89 plates, index. The Macmillan Company, New York. Revised edition, 1946.

Type Specimens of Reptiles and Amphibians in the United States National Museum, by Doris M. Cochran. 291 pp., index. Bulletin 220, The Smithsonian Institution. Superintendent of Documents, U. S. Government Printing Office, Washington, D. C. 1961.

Turtles of the United States and Canada, by Clifford H. Pope. 343 pp., illus., index. Alfred A. Knopf, Inc., New York. 1949.

Rusty Lizard, The: A Population Study, by W. Frank Blair. 185 pp., illus. (figs. & tables), index. University of Texas Press, Austin. 1960.

Voice of the Desert: A Naturalist's Interpretation, by Joseph Wood Krutch. 223 pp., illus. William Sloane Associates, New York. 1955.

Wellsprings of Life, The, by Isaac Asimov. 238 pp., illus., index. Abelard-Schuman, New York. 1960.

World of Amphibians and Reptiles, The, by Robert Mertens, trans. by W. H. Parker, 207 pp., illus., index. McGraw-Hill Book Company, Inc., New York. 1960.

FOR YOUNGER READERS:

Eyes of Nature, by Norman D. Harris (Prepared with the cooperation of the National Audubon Society). 46 pp., line drawings. Nelson Doubleday, Inc., Garden City, New York. 1955.

Introducing Dragons, photographs and text by V. J. Stanek, trans. by Sylva Souckova. Spring Books, London, England.

Natural History of the Southwest, The, edited by William A. Burns. 141 pp. and index., illus. Franklin Watts, Inc., New York. 1960.

Prehistoric Animals, by William E. Scheele. 125 pp., illus. The World Publishing Company, Cleveland and New York. 1954.

Reptiles Round the World, by Clifford H. Pope. 194 pp., illus., index. Alfred A. Knopf, New York. 1957.

Wonderful World of Life, The (The Story of Evolution), by Julian Huxley. 69 pp., illus., index. Garden City Books, Garden City, New York. 1958.

INDEX